# STRUCTURES IN SPELLING

## Words with Prefixes, Roots, and Suffixes

Tim Brown & Deborah F. Knight

New Readers Press

## About the Authors

Deborah F. Knight began her teaching career in the early 1970s and has taught both reading and English in urban, suburban, and rural settings. Since 1984, Ms. Knight has served as Coordinator of the Learning Disabilities Assistance Program at Onondaga Community College in Syracuse, New York. Working closely with the students there, she has helped them to develop strategies for improving their reading, writing, spelling, and study skills.

Tim Brown has worked with developing and remedial readers and writers since 1978. He teaches courses in spelling as well as freshman composition and literature at Onondaga Community College. He also serves as Senior Professional Tutor at the college's Writing Skills Center, where he has a special interest in teaching spelling to developing and remedial writers and ESL students.

Knight and Brown are also the authors of the *Patterns in Spelling* series published by New Readers Press.

Structures in Spelling
ISBN 0-88336-151-5

Copyright © 1992
New Readers Press
Division of ProLiteracy Worldwide
1320 Jamesville Avenue, Syracuse, New York 13210
www.newreaderspress.com

Printed in the United States of America
19  18  17  16  15  14  13  12  11

All proceeds from the sale of New Readers Press materials
support literacy programs in the United States and worldwide.

**Sponsoring Editor:** Christina M. Jagger
**Editors:** Mary Hutchison, Mary Mackay
**Design:** Kathleen T. Bates
**Production:** Sharon Naftal
**Cover Design:** The WD Burdick Company

# Table of Contents

# Terms and Symbols Used in This Book

**adjective**

A describing word. Example: *hot*

**affix**

A prefix or suffix; a part that is added to a root to change its meaning. Examples: *pre-* and *-ion* in *prediction*

**combining form**

A word part that may be used as either a root or an affix. Example: *photo* in *photograph* and *telephoto*

**homophone**

One of two or more words that sound the same but have different meanings, spellings, and origins. Example: *patience* and *patients*

**morpheme**

A group of letters with meaning. Prefixes, roots, suffixes, and combining forms are all morphemes.

**noun**

A word that names a person, place, thing, quality, or action. Example: *prediction*

**prefix**

A part added to the beginning of a root to change its meaning. Example: *pre-* in *predict*

**root**

The base of a word, to which other parts are added. Example: *dict* in *predict*

**schwa**

A vowel sound that usually occurs in unstressed syllables in English as heard in the first syllable of *against;* also the symbol /ə/ often used to represent the sound.

**suffix**

A part added to the end of a root to change its meaning. Example: *-ion* in *prediction*

**variant forms**

Morphemes that are similar in origin, spelling, and meaning. Examples: the prefixes *in-* and *im-;* the roots *scribe* and *script;* the suffixes *-able* and *-ible;* and the combining forms *thermo* and *therm*

**verb**

A word that expresses action, occurrence, or existence. Example: *predict*

**/k/**

A letter between slashes indicates a sound rather than a spelling. Example: /k/ is the sound produced by the letter *k*.

**/ə/**

This indicates the schwa sound.

**/ā/**

A straight line (macron) over a vowel indicates the long vowel sound.

**Basics**

**Some Basic Concepts**

**1** **What Are the Structures in Spelling?**

Many English words are formed by putting parts of words together. Some parts get used over and over again to spell thousands of different words. Learning to recognize and spell the word parts is easier than learning the spelling of each individual word.

The lessons in this book will help you to recognize and spell word parts. They will also help you to review and practice some patterns for putting parts together. If you know how to spell the common word parts and how to put them together, the building and spelling of many words becomes automatic.

**2** **Word Parts Have Meaning**

Most words are built from parts that have meanings. For example, *dict* means *to tell,* and *pre-* means *before. Predict* means *to tell before,* or to tell about something before it happens.

Look at the following group of words. All of these words are built using the word part *dict,* meaning *to tell.*

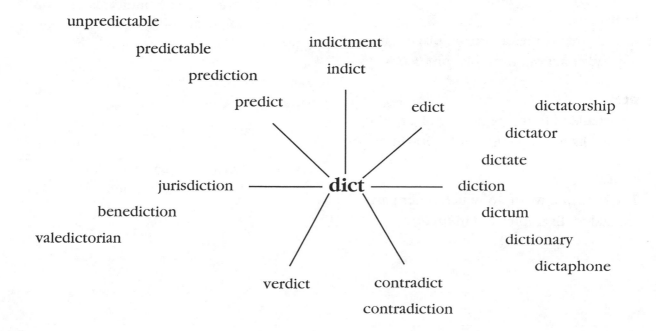

This diagram does not include every word with the part *dict,* but it gives you an idea of how many different words can be formed using one part.

Our minds can organize and remember more words when we understand the relationships among them. If you know the meanings and spellings of word parts, many new words will be easier to learn. Some words you may have heard but never written will be easier to spell.

## 3 Word Origins

The English we use is based mostly on older languages. Most English words come from Latin, Greek, or Old English. Many dictionaries give information about word origins. Usually this information is abbreviated. It may follow the pronunciation guide that appears after a word in the dictionary, or it may come after all the definitions.

All dictionaries do not give the same information about word origins. Here are three examples of how the origin of *predict* may be given, depending on which dictionary you use.

**Example 1:** [L. *praedictus,* pp. of *praedicere,* fr. *prae-* pre- + *dicere* to say]

**Example 2:** [Lat. *praedicere*: *prae-,* before + *dicere,* to say]

**Example 3:** [*pre* before + *dict* tell <Latin]

Now look up *predict* in your dictionary. Copy what it gives about the origin of *predict* on the line below.

predict: _____

Look up the following words. Does your dictionary show the parts of each word? Copy what the dictionary gives about the origin and parts on the line following each word.

impart _____

pretend _____

_____

suppose_____

_____

triceratops _____

_____

# 4 Using the Dictionary

Most English words built from parts come from Latin and Greek. Knowing the language of origin may help you to understand or to spell a word. For example, words from Greek usually spell /f/ as *ph*. If you know that *graph* is from Greek, you may find it easier to spell *telegraph, geography,* or *photograph.*

Use a dictionary to find out the language of origin of each of the following words. Write the answers on the lines provided.

1. adapt _____
2. border _____
3. dictate _____
4. emerge _____
5. bludgeon _____

6. tycoon _____
7. graphic _____
8. neighbor _____
9. technology _____
10. microscope _____

Notice how many of these words come from Latin or Greek.

# 5 The Names of Word Parts

In order to talk about words that are built from parts, you need some terms for the parts of words. You may know these already.

**Prefix:** a part added to the beginning of a root to change its meaning.
Example: *pre-* in *predict*

**Root:** the base of a word, to which other parts are added.
Example: *dict* in *predict*

**Suffix:** a part added to the end of a root to change its meaning.
Example: *-ion* in *prediction*

**Affix:** a prefix or suffix; a part that is added to a root to change its meaning.
Examples: *pre-* and *-ion*

**Combining form:** a word part that may be used as either a root or an affix.
Example: *photo* in *photograph* and *telephoto*

**Morpheme:** a group of letters with meaning. Prefixes, roots, suffixes, and combining forms are all morphemes.

**Variant forms:** morphemes that are similar in origin, spelling, and meaning.
Examples: the prefixes *in-* and *im-,* the roots *scribe* and *script,* the suffixes *-able* and *-ible,* and the combining forms *thermo* and *therm.*

# 6 Word Building

In this book, the plus sign (+) indicates the process of word building: *re + spect* indicates that *respect* is to be built.

Join the morphemes as indicated below to make words. Write the words on the lines provided. Do not add, drop, or change any letters.

| Prefixes | Roots | Suffixes | Whole words |
|---|---|---|---|
| 1. dis | + ease | | _____ |
| 2. | press | + ure | _____ |
| 3. re | + spect | + ful | _____ |
| 4. pre | + dict | + able | _____ |
| 5. intro | + duct | + ion | _____ |

Although you do sometimes add, drop, or change letters, the process of word building is generally as simple as in the above examples.

# 7 Challenge Word Building

On a separate piece of paper, combine the morphemes below to build as many words as you can. Use as few or as many parts as you need for each word. Use a dictionary if you are unsure of a word.

| Prefixes | Roots | Suffixes |
|---|---|---|
| con- | tent | -al |
| in- | vent | -ly |
| un- | | -ion |
| | | -ious |
| | | -ive |

How many words did you build? _____

# Practice

## Using Morphemes

Lesson 1 described morphemes, the building blocks of language. If you learn about morphemes and how to combine them, you can spell thousands of words. In this lesson you will practice using morphemes in various ways.

## 1 Reviewing Terms

Write one of the following terms in each blank below, beside the appropriate definition.

| | | | |
|---|---|---|---|
| affix | morphemes | suffix | root |
| combining form | prefix | variant forms | |

1. Word parts that have meaning: _____

2. A word part added to the beginning of a word: _____

3. A word part added to the end of a word: _____

4. The part of a word to which other parts are added: _____

5. A prefix or suffix: _____

6. Morphemes that are similar in spelling and meaning: _____

7. A word part that can be both a root and an affix: _____

## 2 Word Building

Join the morphemes that follow to build whole words. Write the words on the lines provided.

1. re + fer _____

2. sub + mit _____

3. re + ceive _____

4. sub + scribe _____

5. re + cept + ion _____

6. re + fer + ence _____

7. sub + script + ion _____

8. ex + cept + ion + al _____

# 3 Discovering How Words Are Built

**Part A.** The Glossary of Morphemes at the back of this book gives the meanings of all the morphemes presented in this text. Look up each morpheme below and write the meaning on the line provided.

de- _____     sup- _____

ex-_____      trans- _____

im-_____      port-_____

re- _____

**Part B.** Now write a definition for each of the following words, using the definitions of the morphemes above.

1. report _____

2. export _____

3. import _____

4. transport _____

**Part C.** On a separate piece of paper, add the prefixes and suffixes below to the root *port* to build as many words as you can. Use a dictionary if you are unsure of a word.

| Prefixes | Root | Suffixes |
|----------|------|----------|
| de-      | port | -able    |
| ex-      |      | -er      |
| im-      |      | -ive     |
| re-      |      | -ment    |
| sup-     |      |          |
| trans-   |      |          |

## 4 Taking Words Apart

Divide the following words into morphemes and write each one under the correct heading. Use the glossary if you are unsure of any. The first one is done for you.

|  | **Prefixes** | **Roots** | **Suffixes** |
|---|---|---|---|
| 1. concept | con | cept | |
| 2. transmit | _____ | _____ | |
| 3. transcribe | _____ | _____ | |
| 4. reception | _____ | _____ | _____ |
| 5. preference | _____ | _____ | _____ |
| 6. exclusive | _____ | _____ | _____ |
| 7. subscription | _____ | _____ | _____ |
| 8. exceptional | _____ | _____ | _____ | _____ |

## 5 Recognizing Morphemes

Below is a list of morphemes. Write each morpheme under the correct heading. Use the glossary if necessary. The first one is done for you.

| ✓ -al | ex- | -ion | -ness | re- |
|---|---|---|---|---|
| cord | form | -ly | pend | sort |
| -er | inter- | mand | pre- | trans- |

| **Prefixes** | **Roots** | **Suffixes** |
|---|---|---|
| _____ | _____ | -al |
| _____ | _____ | _____ |
| _____ | _____ | _____ |
| _____ | _____ | _____ |
| _____ | _____ | _____ |

# 6 Recognizing Variant Forms

Some words have forms that are spelled differently. For instance, *take* and *took* are different forms of the same word. The spelling changes depending on how the word is used in phrases or sentences.

As you learned in Lesson 1, morphemes that are similar in spelling and meaning are called variant forms. Variant forms of the same morpheme are listed together in this book. *Scribe* and *script* are examples of variant forms. Look at these sentences:

> I sub*scribe* to the local newspaper.
> My sub*script*ion runs out soon.

Usually the variant forms are alike enough in spelling that their relationship is fairly obvious. List A below contains several morphemes that have variant forms. List B has one variant form for each morpheme in List A. Match the variant forms in Lists A and B and write the pairs on the lines provided. Use the glossary if you need to.

| List A | List B | Pairs of variant forms |
|--------|--------|------------------------|
| -ance  | merse  | _____ |
| cede   | im-    | _____ |
| fact   | miss   | _____ |
| -ery   | -ant   | _____ |
| in-    | tense  | _____ |
| merge  | ef-    | _____ |
| sub-   | -ary   | _____ |
| tend   | cess   | _____ |
| ex-    | fect   | _____ |
| mit    | sup-   | _____ |

# 7 Creating and Using Words

Add a prefix, suffix, or both to each root below to create a word. Then use the words in original phrases or short sentences. You may use affixes from this lesson, from the glossary, or any others that you know. The first one is started for you.

|  | Whole words | Phrases or sentences |
|---|---|---|
| 1. sist | resist | |
| 2. port | | |
| 3. vent | | |
| 4. clude | | |

# 8 Taking Apart and Rebuilding Words

**Part A.** Divide the following words into prefixes and roots and write each part under the correct heading. Check individual morphemes in the glossary if necessary.

| | Prefixes | Roots | | | Prefixes | Roots |
|---|---|---|---|---|---|---|
| 1. infuse | | | | 4. import | | |
| 2. resign | | | | 5. expose | | |
| 3. deduct | | | | 6. conceive | | |

**Part B.** Now combine the prefixes and roots above in different ways to form 10 new words. Write them on the lines provided. Check a dictionary if you are unsure of any combination. The first one is done for you.

confuse _____   _____

_____   _____

_____   _____

_____   _____

_____   _____

# Suffixes

## Patterns for Adding Suffixes

The spelling of a root sometimes changes when a suffix is added. This lesson reviews four common patterns in which this happens. You will be using these patterns often.

## 1 The *y* to *i* Pattern

Study the pattern below.

> When adding a suffix to a word that ends in a consonant plus *y*, change the *y* to *i*, unless the suffix begins with *i*.

**Part A.** Combine the following roots and suffixes following the *y* to *i* pattern. Write the new words on the lines provided, and answer the question in the last column.

|  | New words | Was *y* changed to *i*? |
|---|---|---|
| 1. supply + er | _____ | _____ |
| 2. crazy + ness | _____ | _____ |
| 3. imply + ing | _____ | _____ |
| 4. merry + ly | _____ | _____ |
| 5. happy + ness | _____ | _____ |

**Part B.** Divide the following words into morphemes and write each one under the correct heading. The first one is done for you.

|  | Prefixes | Roots | Suffixes | |
|---|---|---|---|---|
| 1. replying | re | ply | ing | |
| 2. loneliness | | _____ | _____ | _____ |
| 3. unhappily | _____ | _____ | _____ | |
| 4. greediness | | _____ | _____ | _____ |
| 5. compliance | _____ | _____ | _____ | |

## 2 The Silent *e* Pattern

Study the pattern below.

........................................................................................................................

The silent *e* at the end of a root is usually dropped when a suffix that starts with a vowel is added. The silent *e* is not dropped if the suffix starts with a consonant.

........................................................................................................................

**Part A.** Combine the following root words and suffixes following the silent *e* pattern. Write the new words on the lines provided.

1. advise + er _____

2. taste + less _____

3. diverse + ity _____

4. ignore + ant _____

5. repute + able _____

6. reverse + ible _____

7. compose + er _____

8. confuse + ion _____

9. emerge + ency _____

10. require + ment _____

**Part B.** Divide the following words into morphemes and write each one under the correct heading. If you are unsure of the spelling of a morpheme, look it up in the glossary at the back of this book. Then write the answer to the question in the final column. The first one is done for you.

| | Prefixes | Roots | Suffixes | Was *e* dropped? |
|---|---|---|---|---|
| 1. service | | serve | ice | yes |
| 2. careful | | | | |
| 3. definite | | | | |
| 4. receiver | | | | |
| 5. incurable | | | | |
| 6. approval | | | | |
| 7. universal | | | | |
| 8. improvement | | | | |

# 3  Doubling Pattern 1

Study the pattern below.

If a word has one syllable, one vowel, and ends in one consonant, double the final consonant before adding an ending that begins with a vowel. Do not double a final *w* or *x*.

**Part A.** Look at the chart below. If a word has one syllable, one vowel, or one final consonant, check the appropriate column. If you check all three columns and the suffix begins with a vowel, double the final consonant before adding the suffix. Write the whole word in the last column. The first one is done for you. Remember: Don't double *w* or *x*.

| | One syllable? | One vowel? | One final consonant? | | Whole words |
|---|---|---|---|---|---|
| 1. rig | ✓ | ✓ | ✓ | + ing | rigging |
| 2. hot | | | | + est | |
| 3. finish | | | | + ing | |
| 4. box | | | | + er | |
| 5. drug | | | | + ist | |

**Part B.** Combine the following roots and suffixes following Doubling Pattern 1. Write the words on the lines provided.

1. slip + er _____

2. fix + ed _____

3. tip + ed _____

4. rub + ery _____

5. bow + ing _____

6. shut + er _____

7. drum + er _____

8. fish + ing _____

9. jump + ing _____

10. design + ed _____

# 4 Doubling Pattern 2

Study the pattern below.

If a word has more than one syllable, look at the last syllable. If the last syllable has one vowel, ends in one consonant, and is accented, double the final consonant before adding a suffix that begins with a vowel. Do not double a final *w* or *x*.

**Part A.** Look at the words below. If the last syllable has one vowel, one final consonant, or is accented, check the appropriate column. If you check all three columns and the suffix begins with a vowel, double the final consonant before adding the suffix. Write the whole word in the last column. The first one is done for you.

| Last syllable: | Has one vowel? | One final consonant? | Is accented? | | Whole words |
|---|---|---|---|---|---|
| 1. transmit | ✓ | ✓ | ✓ | + al | transmittal |
| 2. propel | | | | + er | |
| 3. admit | | | | + ance | |
| 4. profit | | | | + able | |
| 5. occur | | | | + ence | |

**Part B.** Join the root words and suffixes below following Doubling Pattern 2, and write the new words on the lines provided.

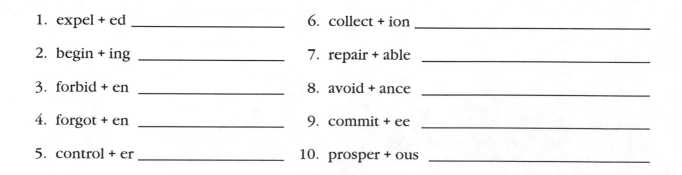

1. expel + ed _____

2. begin + ing _____

3. forbid + en _____

4. forgot + en _____

5. control + er _____

6. collect + ion _____

7. repair + able _____

8. avoid + ance _____

9. commit + ee _____

10. prosper + ous _____

# 5 Reviewing Patterns for Adding Suffixes

Below are the patterns reviewed in this lesson.

..........................................................................

1. **Changing _y_ to _i_:** When adding a suffix to a word that ends in a consonant plus _y_, change the _y_ to _i_ unless the ending begins with _i_.

2. **Silent _e_ Pattern:** Drop the final _e_ if the suffix begins with a vowel.

3. **Doubling Pattern 1:** Double the final consonant if the word has one syllable, one vowel, one final consonant, and the suffix begins with a vowel. Do not double _w_ or _x_.

4. **Doubling Pattern 2:** With words of more than one syllable, double the final consonant if the last syllable has one vowel, one final consonant, and is accented and if the suffix starts with a vowel.

..........................................................................

Remove the ending from each word listed below. Then write the number of the pattern above that had been followed when the ending was added. The first one is done for you.

|  | Root words | Patterns |
|---|---|---|
| 1. fitting | fit | 3 |
| 2. pliable | | |
| 3. refusal | | |
| 4. refinery | | |
| 5. variance | | |
| 6. recurring | | |
| 7. beginning | | |
| 8. happiness | | |
| 9. supervisor | | |
| 10. transmitter | | |

## 1 Recognizing Suffixes

In each group of words below, underline the suffixes listed on the left.

*-ful*      *full of*

| useful | careful | faithful |
|--------|---------|----------|
| helpful | thankful | cheerful |

*-less*      *without, lacking*

| useless | careless | lifeless |
|---------|----------|----------|
| helpless | thankless | hopeless |

*-ly*      *in the manner of*

| usefully | carelessly | happily |
|----------|------------|---------|
| helplessly | thankfully | willingly |

*-ward*      *direction*

| eastward | afterward | toward |
|----------|-----------|--------|
| backward | homeward | upwardly |

## 2 Word Building

Join the morphemes that follow to build whole words. Write the words on the lines provided.

1. like + ly _____

2. lone + ly _____

3. play + ful _____

4. awk + ward _____

5. speech + less _____

6. fear + less + ly _____

7. grate + ful + ly _____

8. out + ward + ly _____

9. breath + less + ly _____

10. thought + ful + ly _____

## 3 Reviewing Terms

Fill in the blanks in the definitions below.

1. A group of letters with meaning is called a _____.

2. A base to which affixes can be added is called a _____.

3. A _____ is added to the beginning of a word to change its meaning.

4. A part added to the end of a word to change its meaning is called a _____.

5. _____ are morphemes that are similar in spelling and meaning.

6. Prefixes and suffixes are _____.

## 4 Taking Words Apart

Divide the following words into morphemes and write each one under the correct heading. Check the suffixes in the glossary and change letters if necessary.

|  | Roots | Suffixes | |
|---|---|---|---|
| 1. happily | _____ | _____ | |
| 2. forward | _____ | _____ | |
| 3. readily | _____ | _____ | |
| 4. thankful | _____ | _____ | |
| 5. hopefully | _____ | _____ | _____ |
| 6. truthfully | _____ | _____ | _____ |
| 7. hurriedly | _____ | _____ | _____ |
| 8. inwardly | _____ | _____ | _____ |
| 9. helplessly | _____ | _____ | _____ |
| 10. wonderfully | _____ | _____ | _____ |

## 5 Adding Suffixes to Words That End in a Consonant Plus *y*

Add the suffix to each word below, and write the new word on the line provided. Remember to change the *y* to *i* if necessary.

1. lazy + ly _____
2. easy + ly _____
3. penny + less _____

4. sleepy + ly _____
5. beauty + ful _____
6. way + ward _____

## 6 Creating and Using Words

From each word listed below, create two new words by adding one or more of the following suffixes. Then use the new words in phrases or short sentences. The first one is started for you.

*-ful*        *-less*        *-ly*        *-ward*

| | New words | Phrases or sentences |
|---|---|---|
| 1. law | lawless | _____ |
| | lawfully | _____ |
| 2. tact | _____ | _____ |
| | _____ | _____ |
| 3. pain | _____ | _____ |
| | _____ | _____ |
| 4. home | _____ | _____ |
| | _____ | _____ |
| 5. thought | _____ | _____ |
| | _____ | _____ |

## 1 Recognizing Suffixes

In each group of words below, underline the suffixes listed on the left.

-hood          *state, quality, or condition of*

| adulthood | statehood | falsehood |
| motherhood | neighborhood | likelihood |

-ness          *state, quality, condition, or degree of*

| darkness | carelessness | uselessness |
| helpfulness | thankfulness | homelessness |

-ment          *state, act, or process of*

| movement | arrangement | government |
| measurement | development | involvement |

-ship          *state, quality, or condition of; skill*

| hardship | relationship | workmanship |
| friendship | companionship | apprenticeship |

## 2 Word Building

Join the morphemes that follow to build whole words. Write the words on the lines provided. Remember to change *y* to *i* if necessary.

1. weak + ness _____

2. child + hood _____

3. state + ment _____

4. equip + ment _____

5. father + hood _____

6. own + er + ship _____

7. champion + ship _____

8. re + fresh + ment _____

9. friend + ly + ness _____

10. shame + less + ness _____

# 3 Taking Words Apart

Divide the following words into morphemes and write each one under the correct heading. Check the suffixes in the glossary and remember to change letters if necessary.

|  | Roots | Suffixes |  |
|---|---|---|---|
| 1. hardship | _____ | _____ | |
| 2. girlhood | _____ | _____ | |
| 3. fragment | _____ | _____ | |
| 4. township | _____ | _____ | |
| 5. treatment | _____ | _____ | |
| 6. cheerfulness | _____ | _____ | _____ |
| 7. likelihood | _____ | _____ | _____ |
| 8. sleepiness | _____ | _____ | _____ |

# 4 Changing the Meaning of Words

**Part A.** Add one of the following suffixes to each word below to change its meaning. Write the new words on the lines provided. Remember to change *y* to *i* if necessary. The first one is done for you.

*-hood*        *-ness*        *-ment*        *-ship*

1. sister ____sisterhood____          5. refine _____

2. lazy _____          6. partner _____

3. priest _____          7. require _____

4. gentle _____          8. sportsman _____

**Part B.** On the lines below, write original sentences using two of the new words.

_____

_____

# 5 Completing Words in Sentences

Add one or two of the following suffixes to the root word given under each blank below and write the completed word in the blank. The word you build must make sense in the sentence. The first one is started for you.

-hood          -ment          -ness          -ship

-ful            -less            -ly             -ward

1. What is the _____**likelihood**_____ of that dog being _____?
   like                                                    friend

2. It is _____ that there are so many _____ people.
   disgrace                                            home

3. I appreciated your _____ during my son's _____ .
   thought                                            ill

4. The new _____ resulted in a _____ of our duties.
   owner                                              rearrange

5. That dance is a complex series of _____ and _____ steps.
   back                                                for

# 6 Missing Links

Add a word to link each pair of morphemes or words below. The missing link will form the end of the first word and the beginning of the second word. You can find all the second words in other exercises in this lesson. The number of blanks indicates how many letters are in each missing link. Study the example before you begin.

**Example:** down  t o w n  ship

1. inter __ __ __ __ __ ment          4. die __ __ __ __ ship

2. grand __ __ __ __ __ hood          5. re __ __ __ __ __ ment

3. girl __ __ __ __ __ __ ship          6. foster __ __ __ __ __ __ hood

# Lesson 6 — Suffixes

*-er, -est, -en, and -ery*

## 1 Recognizing Suffixes

In each group of words below, underline the suffixes listed on the left.

| -er, -or | *someone who;* | | | *something that* |
|---|---|---|---|---|
| | driver | jogger | operator | folder |
| | teacher | reader | spectator | refrigerator |

| -er | *more* | | | |
|---|---|---|---|---|
| | bigger | nicer | colder | happier |

| -est | *most* | | | |
|---|---|---|---|---|
| | biggest | nicest | coldest | happiest |

| -en | *made of; cause to be or have; become* | | | |
|---|---|---|---|---|
| | golden | wooden | deafen | fatten |

| -ery, -ary, -ory, -ry | *place where; collection, condition, or practice of* | | | |
|---|---|---|---|---|
| | surgery | library | factory | ministry |
| | machinery | secondary | advisory | carpentry |

## 2 Word Building

Join the morphemes that follow to build whole words. Write the words on the lines provided. Remember to change or drop letters if necessary.

1. sticky + er _____

2. loose + en _____

3. bribe + ery _____

4. dentist + ry _____

5. strange + er _____

6. bright + en _____

7. simple + est _____

8. burgle + ary _____

9. satis + fact + ory _____

10. ad + ministrate + or _____

## 3 Practicing Doubling Patterns 1 and 2

Join the root words and suffixes below. Remember to double the final consonant of the root if necessary.

1.  hid + en _____

2.  can + ery _____

3.  rub + ery _____

4.  pot + ery _____

5.  drum + er _____

6.  sharp + en _____

7.  control + er _____

8.  transmit + er _____

## 4 Variant Forms of *-ery*

The suffix *-ery* has three variant forms: *-ary*, *-ory*, and *-ry*. Often you can determine the spelling of the suffix by the way the word is pronounced. For example, you can hear an *a* in *dictionary*. On the other hand, the suffix in *burglary* is pronounced /ǝry/. The suffixes *-ery* and *-ory* are also pronounced /ǝry/ in many words. If you are not sure which spelling to use, the best strategy is to look the word up in a dictionary.

Add a form of *-ery* to the roots below and write the new words under the appropriate heading. Add or drop letters if necessary. Use a dictionary to check your spelling.

| access | contradict | honor | poet |
| arch | direct | launder | prime |
| brew | found | moment | slip |

| -ery | -ary | -ory | -ry |
| --- | --- | --- | --- |
| _____ | _____ | _____ | _____ |
| _____ | _____ | _____ | _____ |
| _____ | _____ | _____ | _____ |

Use three of the new words in original sentences.

_____

_____

_____

# 5 Discovering Strategies

At the end of a word, *-er* and *-or* sound the same. There are some strategies for choosing the correct spelling of /ər/, however.

**Strategy 1: Probabilities.** The most common spelling of /ər/ at the end of words is *-er*. There are more than five words with the suffix *-er* for every word with *-or*. If you can't use a dictionary and have to guess at the spelling of a word, you should usually use *-er* because that is the most probable spelling of /ər/.

**Strategy 2: Meanings.** The suffix *-er* has two meanings: *someone who or something that* and *more*. The suffix *–or* only means *someone who or something that*. When /ər/ means *more*, it is spelled *-er*.

**Strategy 3: Looking at root words.** The suffixes *-er* and *-or* are added to verbs to change them into nouns meaning *someone who or something that* does an action. The suffix *-or* is added to certain kinds of verbs. Add *-or* to the verbs below and answer the questions that follow.

1. visit _____     5. decorate _____

2. invent _____     6. operate _____

3. conduct _____     7. profess _____

4. elevate _____     8. process _____

What is the last letter in the roots in numbers 1–3? _____

What are the last three letters in the roots in numbers 4–6? _____

What are the last three letters in the roots in numbers 7 and 8? _____

**Pattern:** The suffix *-or* is usually added to roots that end in *t*, *-ate*, or *ess*.

## 6 Completing Words in Sentences

Add one of the following suffixes to the root given under each blank below, and write the completed word in the blank. The word you build must make sense in the sentence.

*-er*   *-or*   *-est*   *-en*   *-ery*   *-ary*   *-ory*   *-ry*

1. _____ was one cause of the Civil War.
    slave

2. The steel _____ provided some _____ employment.
    indust                          tempor

3. The _____ was caught by the _____ _____.
    hijack                          clever          investigate

4. If they _____ the road, will they also fix the _____ parts?
    wide                                          bumpy

5. The _____ was the _____ in recent _____.
    rob                          big                          hist

## 7 Missing Letters

A pair of letters has been omitted twice from each word below. Using only the two-letter morphemes from this lesson, fill in the missing letters to make whole words. The first one is done for you.

1. cat 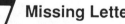 e r e r

2. __ __ light __ __

3. __ __ as __ __

4. h __ __ r __ __

5. l __ __ gth __ __

6. dec __ __ at __ __

7. m __ __ ri __ __

8. che __ __ lead __ __

9. p __ __ form __ __

10. str __ __ gth __ __

11. co __ __ dinat __ __

12. conv __ __ t __ __

# Suffixes

### –*ion* and –*ian*

## 1 Recognizing Suffixes

In each group of words below, underline the suffixes listed on the left.

*-ion*          *act, result, state of*

| direction | taxation | discussion |
| attraction | inspection | persuasion |
| association | contraption | transmission |
| participation | contamination | comprehension |

*-ian*          *person who; of, relating to, belonging to*

| musician | civilian | Asian |
| politician | vegetarian | Italian |
| technician | pedestrian | Christian |

## 2 Word Building

Join the morphemes that follow to build whole words. Write the words on the lines provided. Remember to drop the silent *e* if necessary.

1. Paris + ian _____

2. quest + ion _____

3. physic + ian _____

4. remiss + ion _____

5. convict + ion _____

6. process + ion _____

7. relocate + ion _____

8. celebrate + ion _____

9. automate + ion _____

10. immigrate + ion _____

Say the words you built. Notice that they end in the sound /shən/. Underline the letter that comes before the *-ion* or the *-ian* in these words.

When *-ion* follows *t* or *s,* it creates a spelling problem. Both *-tion* and *-sion* spell /shən/. When *-ian* follows *c,* it also spells /shən/. In the exercises that follow, you will practice some strategies for predicting the spelling of /shən/.

# 3 Words That End in *-tion*

**Strategy 1: Probabilities.** The most common spelling of /shən/ is *-tion*. There are more than seven words that end in *-tion* for every word that ends in *-sion*. If you don't know how to spell a word ending in /shən/ and you can't look it up in a dictionary, you should use *-tion* because that is the most probable spelling of /shən/.

**Strategy 2: Looking at root words.** Sometimes knowing the root word can help you to decide the correct spelling of /shən/. On the lines provided, write the root words for the words below and answer the question that follows.

1. direction _____      3. pollution _____

2. adoption _____      4. participation _____

What is the last consonant in each of these root words? _____

**Pattern:** When a root word ends in *t* or *te,* the ending /shən/ will probably be spelled *-tion.*

**Strategy 3: Extra letters.** Sometimes when the suffix *-ion* is added to a root, other letters are also added. Write the root words for the words below.

1. taxation _____      3. addition _____

2. continuation _____      4. definition _____

Say the words ending in *-ion.* Listen for the other letters that were added to the root.

**Pattern:** When extra letters are added to the root before *-ion,* /shən/ will probably be spelled *-tion.*

Add *-ion* to the words below following these patterns. Say each new word before writing it.

1. react _____      6. qualify _____

2. apply _____      7. protect _____

3. locate _____      8. compete _____

4. satisfy _____      9. transport _____

5. correct _____      10. transform _____

# 4 Words That End in -sion

The second most common spelling of /shən/ is -sion. Here are some strategies for predicting when to use -sion.

**Strategy 1: Root words that end in se.** Write the root words for these words.

1. tension _____

2. television _____

3. revision _____

4. confusion _____

**Pattern:** When a root word ends in se, the silent e is dropped and -ion is added.

**Strategy 2: Root words that end in d or de.** Write the root words for these words.

1. invasion _____

2. explosion _____

3. decision _____

4. extension _____

**Pattern:** When a root word ends in d or de, those letters are often changed to s, and -ion is added.

**Strategy 3: The root vert.** Write the root words for the following words.

1. conversion _____

2. introversion _____

**Pattern:** When -ion is added to words with the Latin root vert, the t is changed to s.

Add -ion to the words below following these strategies.

1. verse _____

2. divert _____

3. revert _____

4. include _____

5. expand _____

6. collide _____

7. precise _____

8. subvert _____

9. transfuse _____

10. conclude _____

## 5 Words That End in *ssion*

In a few words the /shən/ ending is spelled *ssion*. Knowing the root words will help you to know when this spelling is used.

**Part A.** Write the root words for these words.

1. possession _____     2. expression _____

**Pattern:** When the root word ends in *ss*, add *-ion* without changing anything.

**Part B.** Write the root words for the following words.

1. admission _____     2. concession _____

**Pattern:** The *ssion* spelling occurs in words that have the Latin roots *mit* and *cede*.

**Part C.** Add *-ion* to the words below following these patterns.

1. permit _____     4. omit _____

2. profess _____     5. impress _____

3. recede _____     6. intercede _____

## 6 The Suffix *-ian*

The suffix *-ian* is often added to words to indicate a person skilled at certain work or a person who does something.

When *-ian* is added to a word that ends in *c*, the ending is pronounced /shən/. If the root ends in *cs*, the *s* is dropped before adding *-ian*. Add *-ian* to the following words.

1. clinic _____     4. politics _____

2. magic _____     5. pediatrics _____

3. electric _____     6. mathematics _____

**Pattern:** When a word that ends in /shən/ means a person who does something, /shən/ will probably be spelled *-cian*.

# Suffixes

*–ant, –ance, –ent, and –ence*

## 1 Recognizing Suffixes

In each group of words below, underline the suffixes listed on the left.

*-ant*      *inclined to; being in a state of;*                          *someone who*

| redundant | pleasant | hesitant | occupant |
| significant | dominant | expectant | assistant |

*-ance, -ancy*      *state or quality of; action*

| assistance | fragrance | hesitancy | vacancy |
| significance | dominance | expectancy | occupancy |

*-ent*      *inclined to; being in a state of;*                          *someone who*

| innocent | recent | urgent | agent |
| convenient | delinquent | frequent | patient |

*-ence, -ency*      *state or quality of; action*

| innocence | sequence | urgency | agency |
| convenience | patience | frequency | emergency |

## 2 Word Building

Join the morphemes that follow to build whole words. Write the words on the lines provided. Remember to change letters if necessary.

1. defy + ant _____

2. reluct + ant _____

3. exist + ence _____

4. persist + ent _____

5. appear + ance _____

6. insist + ence _____

7. intellig + ent _____

8. adolesc + ent _____

9. attend + ance _____

10. consist + ency _____

## 3 Strategies for Spelling /ənt/, /əns/, and /ənsē/

The suffixes -ant and -ent are pronounced the same way. This is usually true of -ance and -ence as well. Saying the word will not help you spell the suffix because these suffixes nearly always have a schwa sound. The exercises in this lesson will give you some strategies for predicting the spelling of /ənt/, /əns/, and /ənsē/.

**Strategy 1: Using the dictionary.** Looking a word up in a dictionary is the most basic strategy for dealing with these sounds, and even the best spellers use it.

**Strategy 2: Related words.** Words ending in -ant often have related forms ending in -ance or -ancy. Words ending in -ent often have related forms ending in -ence or -ency.

Fill in the blanks in this chart following Strategy 2. The first one is done for you.

| -ant | -ance/-ancy | -ent | -ence/-ency |
|------|-------------|------|-------------|
| extravagant | extravagance | _____ | indulgence |
| _____ | truancy | coherent | _____ |
| ignorant | _____ | existent | _____ |
| _____ | relevancy | _____ | inconsistency |

## 4 Reviewing Patterns: Hard and Soft c and g

The letters c and g each spell two sounds. When c spells /k/ and g spells /g/, we say they are hard. When c spells /s/ and g spells /j/, we say they are soft. The letters that follow the c or g usually signal whether they will be hard or soft. An a usually signals a hard c or g, while an e signals a soft c or g.

Add -ant/-ance/-ancy or -ent/-ence/-ency to each of the roots below and write the words under the appropriate headings. Say each word before you write it, so you know if the c or g is hard or soft.

arrog    dec    dilig    extravag    innoc    signific    urg    vac

| -ant | -ance/-ancy | -ent | -ence/-ency |
|------|-------------|------|-------------|
| _____ | _____ | _____ | _____ |
| _____ | _____ | _____ | _____ |
| _____ | _____ | _____ | _____ |
| _____ | _____ | _____ | _____ |

## 5 Another Related-Word Strategy: Words That End in *-ant*

In Lesson 7 you added *-ion* to verbs to form nouns. Many nouns formed this way end in *-ation*. When there is a related word ending in /ənt/, the suffix will usually be spelled *-ant*. Fill in the chart below. The first one is done for you.

| Verbs | Nouns ending in *-ation* | Words ending in *-ant* |
|-------|--------------------------|------------------------|
| 1. irritate | irritation | irritant |
| 2. expect | | |
| 3. consult | | |
| 4. occupy | | |
| 5. hesitate | | |
| 6. tolerate | | |
| 7. immigrate | | |
| 8. dominate | | |
| 9. intoxicate | | |
| 10. participate | | |

## 6 Discovering a Pattern: Words That End in *-ent/-ence/-ency*

Fill in the blanks in the chart below. Then answer the questions that follow.

| Words ending in *-ent* | Related words ending in *-ence/-ency* |
|------------------------|---------------------------------------|
| 1. frequent | |
| 2. | delinquency |
| 3. eloquent | |
| 4. | consequence |

1. What two letters come before the suffix in all of these words? _____

2. When a root ends in *qu,* what suffixes are usually used? _____

# 7 Words in Context: A Strategy for Homophones

Say the pairs of words below and listen to the way they sound.

assistants—assistance          patients—patience

The plural suffixes *-ants* and *-ents* sound like *-ance* and *-ence*. When these words are pronounced by themselves, there is no way to tell them apart. The correct spelling depends upon how they are used in context.

Fill in the blanks in the following sentences with one of the words below the blank. The word must make sense in the sentence. Remember that the word ending in *nts* will be a noun meaning *more than one person or thing.*

1. We asked how to get to the mayor's _____.
                                          residence/residents

2. Only 52 percent of the _____ voted in the last election.
                              residence/residents

3. He supervises several _____.
                              assistance/assistants

4. When my car broke down, I had to call for _____.
                                                assistance/assistants

5. That doctor has a great deal of _____.
                                      patience/patients

6. That doctor has a great many _____.
                                    patience/patients

7. The bride had five _____ in the wedding.
                        attendance/attendants

8. Clara's son had perfect _____ in school last year.
                              attendance/attendants

### Suffixes Presented in This Unit

| | | | |
|---|---|---|---|
| -ance | -ency | -hood | -ness |
| -ancy | -ent | -ian | -or |
| -ant | -er | -ion | -ory |
| -ary | -ery | -less | -ry |
| -en | -est | -ly | -ship |
| -ence | -ful | -ment | -ward |

## 1 Adding Suffixes to Change the Meaning of Words

Add one or more of the suffixes above to each word below to make a new form of the word. Remember to add, drop, or change letters if necessary. Write the new words on the lines provided.

1. act _____

2. like _____

3. help _____

4. fresh _____

5. direct _____

6. refine _____

7. expect _____

8. discuss _____

9. civil _____

10. advise _____

11. ignore _____

12. indulge _____

13. inspect _____

14. intrude _____

15. consist _____

16. occupy_____

Use two of the new words in original sentences.

_____

_____

## 2 Jumbled Word Building

Build words by putting the morphemes below in the correct order. Write the words on the lines provided. Remember to add, drop, or change letters if necessary. The first one is done for you.

1. spect re ful __respectful__

2. less ly self _____

3. ful stress ly _____

4. ug ness ly _____

5. er lead ship _____

6. ly like hood _____

7. ate spect or _____

8. en deep ed _____

9. y wealth est _____

10. pent ry car _____

11. fresh re ment _____

12. for straight ward _____

## 3 Predicting the Spelling of /ər/

**Part A.** Complete the sentences below.

1. The most common way to spell /ər/ at the end of a word is _____.

2. The most common spelling after words ending in *-ate*, *t*, or *ess* is _____.

3. When /ər/ means *more*, it is spelled _____.

**Part B**. Add *-er* or *-or* to the words below and write them in the correct column.

| angry | carry | catch | collect | custom |
| fast | listen | legislate | messy | operate |
| perform | investigate | radiate | true | young |

**-er**             **-er**                     **-or**

_____     _____             _____

_____     _____             _____

_____     _____             _____

_____     _____             _____

_____     _____             _____

## 4 Completing Words in Sentences

Add one of the following forms of the suffix *-ery* to the root given under each blank below and write the completed word in the blank. The word you build must make sense in the sentence.

*-ery*        *-ary*        *-ory*        *-ry*

1. Paying taxes isn't _____, it's _____.
   <br>volunt                         obligat

2. That _____ is _____ to build car bodies.
   <br>machin                         necess

3. Using a _____ is one way to build _____.
   <br>diction                         vocabul

4. There was a _____ at the _____ last night.
   <br>burgl                         fact

5. The _____ from the window is quite _____.
   <br>scen                         ordin

6. The _____ room in our building is _____.
   <br>laund                         satisfact

## 5 Reviewing and Practicing Strategies for Spelling /shən/

**Part A.** Complete the sentences below.

1.. The most common spelling of /shən/ is _____.

2. When a root word ends in *t* or *te,* or when other letters are added to the root before *-ion*, /shən/ is probably spelled _____.

3. When a root word ends in *se, d,* or *de,* /shən/ is probably spelled _____.

4. In words with the Latin root *vert*, /shən/ is spelled _____, and in words with the roots *mit* or *cede* or when a root ends in *ss,* /shən/ is spelled _____.

5. When a word ending in /shən/ means a person who does something, /shən/ is probably spelled _____.

**Part B.** Add *-ion* or *-ian* to each root word below. Write the new words on the lines provided. Remember to add, drop, or change letters if necessary.

1. erode _____

2. ignite _____

3. music _____

4. inform _____

5. educate _____

6. product _____

7. confuse _____

8. transmit _____

9. relax _____

10. politics _____

11. correct _____

12. confess_____

13. electric _____

14. pervert _____

15. concede _____

16. appreciate _____

# 6  Reviewing and Practicing Strategies for Spelling /ənt/, /əns/, and /ənsē/
**Part A.** Complete the sentences below.

1. Words ending in *-ent* often have related forms ending in _____ or _____.

2. Words ending in *-ance* or *-ancy* often have related forms ending in _____.

3. If you hear a soft *c* or *g* at the end of a root word, use the suffixes _____,

   _____, or _____.

4. A hard *c* or *g* will be followed by the suffixes _____, _____, or _____.

5. After *qu*, /ənt/ is spelled _____ and /əns/ is spelled _____.

**Part B.** Add *-ant* or *-ent* to the roots below. Write the new words on the lines provided.

1. urg _____

2. dilig _____

3. frequ _____

4. domin _____

5. immigr _____

6. occup _____

7. arrog _____

8. expect _____

9. subsequ _____

10. magnific _____

# Lesson 9 — Prefixes

## *a–, ad–, in–, and un–*

## 1 Recognizing Prefixes

In each group of words below, underline the prefixes listed on the left.

**a-**

*without;*

| | | *on, in; in a state of* | |
|---|---|---|---|
| atypical | amoral | afield | apart |
| asymmetrical | asexual | ashore | aboard |

**ad-, ac-, ap-, as-**

*toward, to, near, or in*

| | | | |
|---|---|---|---|
| adapt | admit | accept | appear |
| addition | adoption | accessory | assistance |
| adhesive | adjustment | approaches | assignment |

**in-, im-**

*in*

| | | | |
|---|---|---|---|
| involved | insert | imminent | impact |
| including | installation | important | impressive |

**in-, im-, il-, ir-**

*not*

| | | | |
|---|---|---|---|
| inhuman | impatient | illegal | irrational |
| incomplete | immature | illogical | irrelevant |
| inexcusable | impossible | illegible | irresistible |

**un-**

*not, opposite of;*

| | | *reverse an action* | |
|---|---|---|---|
| unkind | unhappy | undo | unfold |
| unusual | unemployed | unload | unlock |
| unnatural | unnecessary | undress | uncover |

## 2  Word Building

Join the morphemes that follow to build whole words. Write the words on the lines provided. Remember to drop the silent *e* if necessary.

1. il + lus + ion _____

2. im + mobile _____

3. un + fast + en _____

4. ap + prove + al _____

5. ad + vent + ure _____

6. im + per + fect _____

7. in + cred + ible _____

8. un + pre + pare + ed _____

9. un + ac + cept + able _____

10. ac + commod + ation _____

## 3  Recognizing Patterns: Prefixes That Change

When prefixes are added to roots, the spelling of the prefix usually does not change. A few prefixes, however, do change when added to roots that start with certain letters. These changes often account for double consonants near the beginning of words. Study the following charts.

### Part A. The Prefix *ad-*

| Prefix | Changes to | Before | Examples |
|--------|-----------|--------|----------|
| ad- | ac- | c | ad + cuse = accuse |
| ad- | ap- | p | ad + pear = appear |
| ad- | as- | s | ad + sume = assume |

In a few words, *ad-* changes to *af-*, *al-*, and *at-* before roots that begin with *f*, *l*, and *t* respectively. Example words are *afflict*, *allocate*, and *attend*.

Join the morphemes below, changing *ad-* if necessary.

1. ad + fect _____

2. ad + point _____

3. ad + semble _____

4. ad + tempt _____

5. ad + here _____

6. ad + cident _____

7. ad + lowance _____

8. ad + proximate _____

**Part B. The Prefix *in-***

| Prefix | Changes to | Before | Examples |
|--------|-----------|--------|----------|
| in- | im- | b, m, or p | in + balance = imbalance |
|  |  |  | in + moral = immoral |
|  |  |  | in + practical = impractical |
| in- | il- | l | in + legible = illegible |
| in- | ir- | r | in + regular = irregular |

Join the morphemes below, changing *in-* if necessary.

1. in + port _____
2. in + ability _____
3. in + mortal _____
4. in + rational _____
5. in + personal _____

6. in + limitable _____
7. in + resistible _____
8. in + legitimate _____
9. in + vulnerable _____
10. in + replaceable _____

## Taking Words Apart

Divide the following words into morphemes and write each one under the correct heading. You may write either the original form of the prefix or the variation used in the word. Check prefixes and suffixes in the glossary if necessary.

|  | Prefixes | Roots | Suffixes |
|--------|----------|-------|----------|
| 1. assorted | _____ | _____ | _____ |
| 2. immortal | _____ | _____ | _____ |
| 3. addiction | _____ | _____ | _____ |
| 4. imported | _____ | _____ | _____ |
| 5. unadjusted | ___ ___ | _____ | _____ |
| 6. appearance | _____ | _____ | _____ |
| 7. unimportant | ___ ___ | _____ | _____ |
| 8. acceptance | _____ | _____ | _____ |

## 5 Changing the Meaning of Words

Add one of the following prefixes to each word below to change its meaning. Write the new words on the lines provided. Use a dictionary if necessary. The first one is done for you.

*in-*    *im-*    *il-*    *ir-*    *un-*

1. pack _____unpack_____

2. moral _____

3. grateful _____

4. passable _____

5. assuming _____

6. important _____

7. active _____

8. perfect _____

9. logical _____

10. pleasant _____

11. adjusted _____

12. resistible _____

Choose two pairs—the original word and the one you formed—and use them in sentences.

_____

_____

## 6 Recognizing Prefixes in Context

Underline the following prefixes in the sentences below.

*a-*    *ad-*    *af-*    *as-*    *at-*    *in-*    *im-*    *ir-*    *un-*

1. Her apathy made her colleagues impatient.

2. That was an unnecessarily dangerous adventure.

3. The company instituted an interim no-smoking policy.

4. The doctor assumed that the infection would clear up.

5. My inexpensive shoes came unglued almost immediately.

6. The forces attacked, but the enemy lines were impenetrable.

7. Most people admit that environmental problems affect everyone.

8. Addiction to alcohol often leads to irrational and unbalanced behavior.

# Lesson 10      Prefixes

*con–, de–, dis–, di–, ex–, and per–*

## 1 Recognizing Prefixes

In each group of words below, underline the prefixes listed on the left.

| *con-, col,* *com-, cor-* | *with, together* | | |
|---|---|---|---|
| congress | conversation | companion | collide |
| connecting | consequence | communicate | correction |

| *de-* | *reverse, remove, reduce* | | |
|---|---|---|---|
| deflate | decay | depreciate | desegregate |
| decrease | deficit | descending | decongestant |

| *dis-, dif-* | *absence; opposite; reverse, remove* | | |
|---|---|---|---|
| distribute | discount | dislike | difficult |
| discontinue | disagreement | dishonest | different |

| *di-* | *separation, twoness* | | |
|---|---|---|---|
| divorce | diverse | divest | dioxide |
| division | diluted | direction | dilemma |

| *ex-, ef-, e-* | *out of, from* | | |
|---|---|---|---|
| export | exterior | effort | eject |
| exception | exclusive | effective | emerge |
| expedition | expanding | emigrate | eruption |

| *per-* | *through; thoroughly* | | |
|---|---|---|---|
| perspire | percolator | perfect | perturbed |
| perforate | permeable | permanent | perseverance |

## 2 Word Building

Join the morphemes that follow to build whole words. Remember to drop the silent *e* if necessary. Write the words on the lines provided.

1. dis + sect _____
2. con + stant _____
3. ef + fici + ent _____
4. di + gress + ion _____
5. ex + pect + ant _____

6. e + limin + ate _____
7. dif + fuse + ion _____
8. per + spect + ive _____
9. com + pare + ed _____
10. de + con + gest + ant _____

## 3 Recognizing Patterns: More Prefixes That Change

When prefixes are added to roots, their spelling usually does not change. The prefixes *con-*, *dis-*, and *ex-*, however, do change when added to roots that begin with certain letters. Study the chart below. Remember that these changes often account for double consonants near the beginning of words.

### The Prefixes *con-*, *dis-*, and *ex-*

| Prefix | Changes to | Before | Examples |
|--------|-----------|--------|----------|
| con- | com- | b, m, or p | con + bine = combine |
| | | | con + merce = commerce |
| | | | con + pete = compete |
| con- | col- | l | con + laborate = collaborate |
| con- | cor- | r | con + respond = correspond |
| dis- | dif- | f | dis + ficult = difficult |
| ex- | ef- | f | ex + fort = effort |

Join the morphemes below, changing *con-*, *dis-*, and *ex-* if necessary.

1. con + pos + ed _____
2. con + rupt + ion _____
3. con + mand + er _____
4. dis + fer + ent _____

5. con + lect + or _____
6. con + bust + ion _____
7. con + vent + ion _____
8. in + ex + fect + ive _____

## 4 Completing Words in Sentences

Add one of the following prefixes to the root given under each blank below, and write the completed word in the blank. The word you build must make sense in the sentence.

con-   com-   de-   dis-   di-   ex-   e-   ef-   per-

1. The loud music from the next apartment is really _____.
   <br>turbing

2. Are you _____ to _____ in this course?
   <br>mitted       celling

3. Please make an _____ to _____ the job today.
   <br>fort          plete

4. My _____ was _____ between two projects.
   <br>centration       vided

5. I _____ him to _____ the _____.
   <br>suaded          amine          vidence

## 5 Challenge Word Building

On a separate piece of paper, combine the morphemes below to build at least 10 words. Use as few or as many morphemes as you need for each word. Remember that the prefixes de- and di- often sound the same, so use a dictionary if you are unsure of a word.

| Prefixes | Roots | Suffixes |
|---|---|---|
| de- | bate | -er |
| di- | cept | -ery |
| dis- | cov | -ive |
| | rect | -ion |
| | script | -or |
| | sign | |

# Prefixes

*pre-, post-, re-, pro-, and mis-*

## 1 Recognizing Prefixes

In each group of words below, underline the prefixes listed on the left.

*pre-*      *before*

| | | |
|---|---|---|
| preview | prejudice | prefix |
| prepared | premature | pretax |
| precaution | preoccupied | prevention |

*post-*      *after, later; behind*

| | | | |
|---|---|---|---|
| postdate | posterity | postscript | postgraduate |
| postpone | posterior | postmortem | posthumously |

*re-*      *back, again, anew*

| | | | |
|---|---|---|---|
| return | release | renew | review |
| retreat | reversal | remember | rediscovered |
| rejection | replacing | reproduction | reappointment |

*pro-*      *forth, forward*

| | | |
|---|---|---|
| proceed | project | prominent |
| progressive | produce | promotion |

*mis-*      *wrongly, badly*

| | | |
|---|---|---|
| mistaken | misdeeds | mislaid |
| mistimed | misbehave | misfortune |
| mistrust | misunderstood | misleading |

## 2 Word Building

Join the morphemes below to build whole words. Write the words on the lines provided.

1. post + nasal _____

2. re + miss + ion _____

3. pro + vis + ion _____

4. pre + cede + ing _____

5. mis + con + duct _____

6. re + ject + ion _____

7. pro + gram +er _____

8. pre + vent + ion _____

9. post + operate + ive _____

10. mis + con + cept + ion _____

## 3 Looking at Meanings: *pre-*, *pro-*, and *per-*

Below is a list of roots. Next to each root is the definition of a word that has that root. Add either *pre-*, *pro-*, or *per-* to the root to make a word that fits the definition. Write the whole word on the line provided. The first one is done for you.

| Roots | Meaning of words | Whole words |
|---|---|---|
| 1. dawn | before dawn | predawn |
| 2. turb | disturb thoroughly | |
| 3. scribe | write beforehand | |
| 4. vade | go through thoroughly | |
| 5. gress | step forward | |
| 6. pare | make ready in advance | |
| 7. mote | move forward or up | |
| 8. mit | give leave, let through | |
| 9. ceed | go forward | |
| 10. caution | care taken in advance | |

## 4 Taking Words Apart

Divide the following words into morphemes and write each one under the correct heading. Remember to add the silent *e* to the root if necessary.

|  | Prefixes | Roots | Suffixes |
|---|---|---|---|
| 1. pretext | _____ | _____ |  |
| 2. provider | _____ | _____ | _____ |
| 3. mistrusted | _____ | _____ | _____ |
| 4. proportion | _____ | _____ | _____ |
| 5. improvising | _____ _____ | _____ | _____ |
| 6. posthumous | _____ | _____ | _____ |
| 7. postponement | _____ | _____ | _____ |
| 8. reappointment | _____ _____ | _____ | _____ |

## 5 Jumbled Morphemes

Use the morphemes in each group below to create three different words. Choose two words from each group and use them in phrases or short sentences. The first one is started for you.

**Phrases or sentences**

1. pro   un   tect   ed

   ___protect___                                    _____

   _____                    _____

   _____

2. pre   able   dict   un

   _____                    _____

   _____                    _____

   _____

3. pro   ion   duct   re

_____     _____

_____     _____

_____


## 6 Recognizing Prefixes in Context

Underline the following prefixes in the sentences below.

     *pre-*     *post-*     *re-*     *pro-*     *mis-*

1. It's redundant to keep on restating the same idea.
2. They requested that the proceeds be shared equally.
3. Juan is a sales representative for a refrigerator company.
4. The rebels were mistaken in persisting in violent behavior.
5. That was a good proposal, and I think you'll be promoted for it.
6. She's not prepared to provide for him or to promise him anything.
7. My father misunderstood how to get reimbursed for medical expenses.
8. We can't prevent this misfortune, but we can postpone telling anyone about it.


## 7 Word Pyramid

Use the letters found in *pre-* to complete the words below. Each word contains the letters *p, r,* and *e* at least once in any order. The first one is done for you.

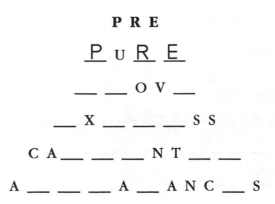

PRE

P u R E

__ __ O V __

__ X __ __ __ S S

C A __ __ __ N T __ __

A __ __ __ A __ A N C __ S

# Review

## Prefixes Presented in This Unit

| | | | |
|---|---|---|---|
| a- | con- | ef- | per- |
| ac- | cor- | ex- | post- |
| ad- | de- | il- | pre- |
| ap- | di- | im- | pro- |
| as- | dif- | in- | re- |
| col- | dis- | ir- | un- |
| com- | e- | mis- | |

**1** ### Adding Prefixes to Change the Meaning of Words

Add one or more of the prefixes above to each word below to make a new form of the word. Write the new words on the lines provided.

1. fort _____

2. port _____

3. press _____

4. cover _____

5. treated _____

6. play _____

7. view _____

8. count _____

9. quest _____

10. formation _____

Use three of the new words in original sentences.

_____

_____

_____

## 2 Reviewing Prefixes That Change

Some prefixes change when they are added to word roots that start with certain letters. These changes often account for double consonants near the beginning of words. Fill in the blanks in the chart below and give one example word for each prefix change.

| Prefix | Changes to | Before | Example words |
|--------|-----------|--------|---------------|
| ad- | | c | |
| ad- | ap- | | |
| in- | | b, m, p | |
| in- | il- | | |
| | ir- | r | |
| con- | com- | | |
| con- | | l | |
| | cor- | r | |
| dis- | dif- | | |
| ex- | | f | |

## 3 Taking Words Apart

Divide the following words into morphemes and write each one under the correct heading. You may write either the original form of the prefix or the variation used in the word.

|  | Prefixes | Roots | Suffixes |
|--|----------|-------|----------|
| 1. consistency | _____ | _____ | _____ |
| 2. deduction | _____ | _____ | _____ |
| 3. discomfort | _____ _____ | _____ | _____ |
| 4. unexciting | _____ _____ | _____ | _____ |
| 5. insertion | _____ | _____ | _____ |
| 6. effortless | _____ | _____ | _____ |

## 4 Creating and Using Words

Add two of the following prefixes to each root listed below to create two different words. Then use each word in an original phrase or short sentence.

*com-   con-   de-   ex-   di-   dis-   re-*

| | **Whole words** | **Phrases or sentences** |
|---|---|---|
| 1. pel | _____ | _____ |
| | _____ | _____ |
| 2. press | _____ | _____ |
| | _____ | _____ |
| 3. serve | _____ | _____ |
| | _____ | _____ |
| 4. vert | _____ | _____ |
| | _____ | _____ |
| 5. duce | _____ | _____ |
| | _____ | _____ |

## 5 Using the Dictionary

For each word below, list all the related words you can think of. When you run out of ideas, check in a dictionary for other related words. The first one is done for you.

**Related words**

1. progress ___ progression, progressive, progressively ___

2. prepare _____

3. mistake _____

4. reproduce _____

5. consider _____

## 6 Completing Words in Sentences

Add one of the following prefixes to the root given under each blank below and write the completed word in the blank. The word you build must make sense in the sentence.

*al-    at-    com-    con-    ef-    ex-    in-    post-    pre-    un-*

1.  The _____ owner _____ tenants to keep animals.
    vious                                     lowed

2.  A warm front is _____ to _____ the storm.
    pected                                  cede

3.  The clean-up was a _____ _____.
    munity                          fort

4.  My girlfriend and I _____ an _____ party last Saturday.
    tended                              cellent

5.  I _____ doing the shopping because I was _____.
    poned                                              well

6.  My friend is _____ in going to the _____.
    terested                                          cert

## 7 Missing Morphemes

One of the prefixes from this unit can be added to every root in each group below. Fill in the missing prefixes to make whole words. Use a different prefix for each group.

1.  _____view    _____duce    _____ceive    _____cess    _____act

2.  _____duce    _____cess    _____duct    _____vide    _____voke

3.  _____mand    _____tract    _____duct    _____fine    _____ceive

4.  _____ceive    _____sist    _____vert    _____duct    _____fine

5.  _____tract    _____ist    _____haust    _____act    _____cess

6.  _____ceive    _____tain    _____mit    _____sist    _____jury

*act, cent, cord, cure, and fact*

## 1 Recognizing Roots

In each group of words below, underline the roots listed on the left.

*act*          *do*

           actor          active          transact          inactivity

           exactly        actually       enactment      interaction

*cent*         *one hundred;*                    *center*

           cent           centimeter     center         concentric

           century        percentage    centralize     concentration

*cord*         *heart*

           cordial        accord        recording

           discordant    accordingly   concordance

*cure*         *care*

           curator        security       accurate       incurable

*fact, fect,*  *make, do*
*fit, fic(t)*

           factory        affects        fitness        fiction

           manufacture   effective     benefit        artificial

           dissatisfaction   infection     profitable     sufficient

## 2 Word Building

Join the morphemes that follow to build whole words. Write the words on the lines provided. Remember to drop the silent *e* or to double letters if necessary.

1. re + cord + er _____

2. pro + fit + ing _____

3. ef + fici + ency _____

4. counter + act + ing _____

5. in + se + cure _____     8. re + act + ion + ary _____

6. per + cent + ile _____     9. in + ac + cure + acy _____

7. per + fect + ion _____     10. af + fect + ion + ate _____

## 3 Taking Words Apart

Divide the following words into morphemes and write each one under the correct heading. Remember to add the silent *e* to the root if necessary.

| | Prefixes | Roots | Suffixes |
|---|---|---|---|
| 1. curable | | _____ | _____ |
| 2. factional | | _____ | _____ _____ |
| 3. discordant | _____ | _____ | _____ |
| 4. benefactor | _____ | _____ | _____ |
| 5. satisfaction | _____ | _____ | _____ |
| 6. accordance | _____ | _____ | _____ |
| 7. prerecorded | _____ _____ | _____ | _____ |
| 8. concentrate | _____ | _____ | _____ |

## 4 Jumbled Morphemes

Use the morphemes in each group below to create three different words. Choose two words from each group and use them in phrases or short sentences.

### Phrases or sentences

1. satis   ory   fact   un   ion

_____       _____

_____       _____

_____

2. suf    ency    fici    ent    in

_____    _____

_____    _____

_____

3. cure    se    in    able    ity

_____    _____

_____    _____

_____

## 5 Adding Roots to Make Complete Words

Write one of the following roots in each blank below to make a whole word that makes sense in the phrase or sentence. Then write the whole word on the right. The first one is done for you.

*act*      *cent*      *cord*      *cure*      *fect/fit/fic*

**Whole words**

1. ex___act___ly right    ___exactly___

2. a difficult sacri_____e    _____

3. an imper_____ match    _____

4. That was a bold _____ion.    _____

5. It's a de_____ive product.    _____

6. Uranium is radio_____ive.    _____

7. ac_____ing to the newspaper    _____

8. the bi_____ennial celebrations    _____

9. Without locks, a house is inse_____.    _____

10. A pro_____able business makes money.    _____

## 1 Recognizing Roots

In each group of words below, underline the roots listed on the left.

*file*                *line, thread; draw a line*

filing          fillet          profile

filament        filigree        defilement


*fine*                *end*

final           infinity        confine

finish          indefinitely    refinement


*found, fund*         *bottom; pour*

foundation      funding         confound

profoundly      refunded        fundamentalist


*fuse*                *pour; melt*

fuse            profusely       refusal

diffuse         confusion       infusion


## 2 Word Building

Join the morphemes that follow to build whole words. Write the words on the lines provided. Remember to drop the silent *e* if necessary.

1. con + found  _____

2. af + fine + ity  _____

3. mis + file + ed  _____

4. re + fuse + ing  _____

5. fin + ance + ial  _____

6. pro + fuse + ion  _____

7. pro + found + ly  _____

8. con + fine + ment  _____

9. un + de + file + ed  _____

10. fund + a + ment + al  _____

# 3 Jumbled Word Building

Build words by putting the morphemes below in the correct order. Write the words on the lines provided. Remember to drop the silent *e* if necessary.

1. al fine ist _____   6. ate ion found _____

2. ed fuse de _____   7. found dumb ed _____

3. file pro ed _____   8. in ion fuse _____

4. ery fine re _____   9. ion fuse con _____

5. ite fine de _____   10. fuse trans ion _____

Say the last three words aloud. Notice how they are pronounced. When you hear the ending /zhən/, it is probably spelled *-sion*.

# 4 Creating and Using Words

Add one or more of the following prefixes or suffixes to each root listed below to create two different words. Remember to add or drop letters if necessary. Then use each word in an original phrase or short sentence.

*con-   de-   pro-   re-*          *-al   -ance   -er   -ion*

|  | **New words** | **Phrases or sentences** |
|---|---|---|
| 1. file | _____ | _____ |
|  | _____ | _____ |
| 2. fine | _____ | _____ |
|  | _____ | _____ |
| 3. found | _____ | _____ |
|  | _____ | _____ |
| 4. fuse | _____ | _____ |
|  | _____ | _____ |

## 5 Recognizing Roots in Context

Underline the following roots in the sentences below.

*file    fine    found/fund    fuse*

1. This is definitely your final chance to refuse.

2. Refile those files when you've finished with them.

3. He was profoundly sorry and apologized profusely.

4. She had a blood transfusion and is confined to bed.

5. If it's not too confusing, let's finalize the plans now.

6. He finally realized how infinite the possibilities were.

7. In all the confusion, the thief managed to confound the clerk.

8. The founders of the company appealed for an infusion of funds.

## 6 Word Pyramids

Use the letters found in *fin* and *fil* to complete the words in each pyramid. Each word contains the letters at the top of the pyramid at least once in any order. Most of the words are from this lesson.

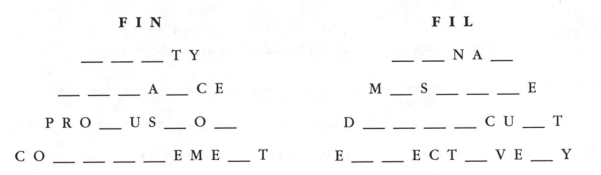

FIN

__ __ __ T Y

__ __ __ A __ C E

P R O __ U S __ O __

C O __ __ __ __ E M E __ T

FIL

__ __ N A __

M __ S __ __ __ E

D __ __ __ __ C U __ T

E __ __ E C T __ V E __ Y

# Lesson 14 — Roots

*mand, merge, muse, pass, and ply*

## 1 Recognizing Roots

In each group of words below, underline the roots listed on the left.

**mand, mend**     *entrust; order*

demanding          mandatory          commendable

commanded          commandment        recommendation

**merge, merse**   *plunge, immerse, dip*

emerge       merger       submergible      immerse

submerge     emergency    reemergence      submersion

**muse**     *gaze, ponder; source of artistic inspiration*

music        musician      musings

museum       amusement     bemused

**pass, pat**     *endure, suffer*

passion          passivity        patient

compassionate    incompatible     impatiently

**ply**     *fold together; fill*

supply       apply          reply

supplier     application    compliment

## 2 Word Building

Join the morphemes that follow to build whole words. Write the words on the lines provided. Remember to drop or change letters if necessary.

1. re + ply + ing _____

2. pass + ion + ate _____

3. ap + ply + ance _____

4. com + pat + ible + ly _____

5. e + merge + ent _____    8. muse + ic + ian + ship _____

6. de + mand + ed _____    9. com + ply + cate + ed _____

7. a + mend + ment _____    10. im + merse + ion _____

Say the last word aloud. Notice how it is pronounced. When you hear the ending /zhən/, it is probably spelled *-sion.*

### Related-Word Strategy

The *y* to *i* pattern is followed when writing words with the root *ply*. Beside each word below, write as many related words using the spelling *pli* as you can. When you run out of ideas, check a dictionary for other forms.

**Related *pli* words**

1. supply    _____

2. apply    _____

3. comply    _____

4. imply    _____

### Looking at Meanings

Add one of the following roots to each partial word below. The word you create must fit the definition on the left. Remember to drop the silent *e* if necessary. Use a dictionary if you are unsure of a word. The first one is done for you.

| *mand/mend* | *merge* | *muse* | *ply* |

| Definitions | Partial words | Words with roots added |
|---|---|---|
| 1. plunge under | sub | submerge |
| 2. exercise authority | com | _____ |
| 3. entertain | a | _____ |
| 4. indicate, suggest | im | _____ |
| 5. mention favorably | recom | _____ |

## 5  Adding Roots to Make Complete Words

Write one of the following roots in each blank below to make a whole word.
Remember to change or drop letters if necessary. Then use the word in an original
phrase or short sentence.

*mand*      *merge*      *muse*      *pass/pat*      *ply*

**Phrases or sentences**

1. e_____ed          _____

2. _____ical         _____

3. a_____ing         _____

4. _____ively        _____

5. sim_____fy        _____

6. com_____er        _____

7. repri_____ed      _____

8. im_____ience      _____

## 6  Recognizing Roots in Context

Underline the following roots in the paragraph below.

*mand/mend*          *pass/pat*          *ply*

The framers of the Constitution of the United States had a complicated task. They did a

commendable job. Ten amendments were then added to encompass rights that were not

originally stated in the Constitution. These amendments apply to all citizens and mandate

basic rights. They include freedom of speech (and the implied freedom of expression),

freedom of assembly, and the right to a fair trial. The remaining amendments were made

later and encompass other rights, but the first 10 amendments alone are known as the Bill

of Rights.

# Lesson 15 — Roots

*pone, port,* and *prove*

## 1 Recognizing Roots

In each group of words below, underline the roots listed on the left.

*pone, pose,*
*post, pound*

*put, place*

| | | | |
|---|---|---|---|
| opponent | position | poster | impound |
| exponent | exposure | posture | expounded |
| component | composition | impostor | compounding |

*port*

*carry*

| | | |
|---|---|---|
| portable | supporter | reported |
| transportation | importance | opportunity |

*prove*

*test*

| | | |
|---|---|---|
| prove | approve | reproved |
| improvement | disapproving | unprovable |

## 2 Word Building

Join the morphemes that follow to build whole words. Write the words on the lines provided. Remember to drop the silent *e* if necessary.

1. com + post _____

2. op + pose _____

3. ex + port + er _____

4. pro + pose + al _____

5. com + pose + er _____

6. un + prove + en _____

7. dis + pose + able _____

8. un + im + port + ant _____

9. post + pone + ment _____

10. dis + ap + prove + al _____

## 3  Adding Roots to Make Complete Words

Write one of the following roots in each blank below to make a whole word. The word must make sense in the phrase or sentence. Remember to drop the silent *e* if necessary. Then write the whole word on the right.

*pone/pose/post/pound*     *port*     *prove*

**Whole words**

1. His ap_____al is needed.          _____

2. an underex_____ed photo          _____

3. the senator's sup_____ers          _____

4. It's a great im_____ment.          _____

5. It is a golden op_____unity.          _____

6. Salt is a sodium com_____.          _____

7. The _____age on the box was $2.45.          _____

8. Trans_____ing two digits creates          _____
an error divisible by nine.

## 4  Changing Morphemes

Remove a prefix or suffix or both from each of the following words and replace it with a different one to form a new word. Use the glossary if necessary. Then use the word you have created in a phrase or sentence. The first one is done for you.

|    | | **New words** | **Phrases or sentences** |
|----|--|------------|----------------------|
| 1. | post*age* | postal | the U.S. postal system |
| 2. | *sup*posed | _____ | _____ |
| 3. | *im*proving | _____ | _____ |
| 4. | *im*ported | _____ | _____ |
| 5. | *com*poser | _____ | _____ |

## 5 Telling the Difference: *Suppose* and *Supposed*

Writing *suppose* instead of *supposed* is a common spelling error. Write the correct form, *suppose* or *supposed*, in each blank below to make sense in the sentence.

1. I am _____ to pass an exam tomorrow. _____ I don't?

2. What do you _____ happened? She was _____ to arrive at 3.

3. I was _____ to work tomorrow. _____ I work today instead?

4. He was _____ to be at home. His mother _____ that he was out playing football.

## 6 Challenge Word Building

On a separate piece of paper, combine the morphemes below to build at least 20 words. Use as few or as many morphemes as you need for each word. Remember to drop the silent *e* if necessary. Use a dictionary if you are unsure of a word.

| Prefixes | Roots | Suffixes |
|----------|-------|----------|
| com- | port | -able |
| dis- | pose | -al |
| ex- | prove | -ation |
| im- | | -ition |
| re- | | -ment |
| sup- | | -ure |
| trans- | | |

# 16 Roots

*tend, quest, sane, sect, serve, and side*

## 1 Recognizing Roots

In each group of words below, underline the roots listed on the left.

*tend, tent, tense*

*stretch*

| extend | extent | pretense |
|---|---|---|
| pretend | intention | extension |
| attendance | attentive | ostensibly |

*quest, quer, quire*

*seek, ask*

| question | conquest | query | inquiry |
|---|---|---|---|
| unquestioning | requested | conqueror | require |

*sane*

*healthy*

| sane | sanitarium | sanitize |
|---|---|---|
| insanity | unsanitary | sanitation |

*sect*

*cut*

| section | sector | bisect |
|---|---|---|
| intersection | dissect | insects |

*serve*

*keep, save; guard*

| reserve | deserve | observant |
|---|---|---|
| preservation | conservative | conservationist |

*side*

*sit, settle*

| reside | president | residue |
|---|---|---|
| residential | subsidiary | dissident |

## 2 Word Building

Join the morphemes that follow to build whole words. Write the words on the lines provided. Remember to change or drop letters if necessary.

1. tend + ency _____

2. quer + y + ed _____

3. sane + it + ary _____

4. sub + side + ize _____

5. dis + sect + ion _____

6. quest + ion + able _____

7. re + quire + ment _____

8. in + sect + i + cide _____

9. in + tent + ion + al _____

10. un + re + serve + ed _____

## 3 Creating and Using Words

From each root listed below, create two new words by adding one or more of the following prefixes or suffixes. Remember to add, drop, or change letters if necessary. Then use the new words in phrases or short sentences.

con-   de-   in-   re-        -ent   -ion   -er

| | New words | Phrases or sentences |
|---|---|---|
| 1. quest | _____ | _____ |
| | _____ | _____ |
| 2. serve | _____ | _____ |
| | _____ | _____ |
| 3. side | _____ | _____ |
| | _____ | _____ |
| 4. tense | _____ | _____ |
| | _____ | _____ |
| 5. tent | _____ | _____ |
| | _____ | _____ |

## 4 Spelling /tenshən/

When *-ion* is added to words with the root *tend*, the root plus the suffix is usually pronounced /tenshən/. The /shən/ ending may be spelled either *-tion* or *-sion*, however. Sometimes there is a related word that will help you remember how to spell the ending. If you are unsure of whether to use *-tion* or *-sion,* the best strategy is to look the word up in the dictionary. Add *-tion* or *-sion* to the partial words below and write the whole word under the correct heading. Use a dictionary if necessary.

*inten*      *atten*      *exten*      *deten*      *preten*      *ten*

**-tion**                                **-sion**

_____          _____

_____          _____

_____          _____

## 5 Recognizing Roots in Context

Underline the following roots in the paragraph below.

*tend/tent*      *quest/quire*      *sane*      *sect*      *serve*      *side*

If you pay attention to the way you spell, you may make some useful observations. When a word gives you particular difficulty, question yourself about how you write it. You might observe that you have a tendency to see if the word "looks right." Notice whether it is built from familiar word parts. If so, dissect the word by breaking it into sections. With other words, the answer to your inquiry might reside in the way the word sounds. In that case, phonetics may deserve a try. Some words simply require memorization. Don't forget, you can preserve your sanity by looking the word up in a dictionary.

# Roots

*ten, sign, sort, stance, test,* and *tail*

## 1 Recognizing Roots

In each group of words below, underline the roots listed on the left.

*ten, tain*          *hold*

| | | | |
|---|---|---|---|
| tenant | tenure | maintain | obtain |
| tenacious | contented | maintenance | contain |

*sign*          *mark, sign*

| | | |
|---|---|---|
| sign | designer | resignation |
| signature | significance | consignment |

*sort*          *chance, lot; go out*

| | | |
|---|---|---|
| sort | resort | presort |
| sorted | assortment | consort |

*stance, stant*          *stand*

| | | |
|---|---|---|
| substance | distance | instance |
| substantial | distantly | constantly |

*test*          *witness*

| | | |
|---|---|---|
| testify | detest | attested |
| testimony | protester | contestant |

*tail*          *cut*

| | | |
|---|---|---|
| tailor | detail | retail |

## 2 Word Building

Join the morphemes that follow to build whole words. Write the words on the lines provided. Remember to change letters if necessary.

1. re + tain _____
2. en + tail + ing _____
3. as + sort + ed _____
4. in + stant + ly _____
5. de + sign + ate _____

6. ten + ure + ed _____
7. de + test + able _____
8. Pro + test + ant _____
9. circum + stance _____
10. out + di + stance _____

## 3 Related-Word Strategy: The Silent *g*

Some words that contain a silent consonant have related words in which that consonant is pronounced. Learning these related words can help you to remember the silent consonant in the root or other related words.

The root *sign* means *mark* or *sign*. This root always conveys that idea, regardless of the pronunciation.

Look up the word *signal* in the dictionary. Write the pronunciation and meaning below.

signal _____

Remembering the word *signal* can help you remember the silent *g* in the word *sign*.

For each word below, write one related word in which the silent *g* is pronounced. Use a dictionary if necessary. The first one is done for you.

1. resign ___resignation___     3. design _____

2. assign _____

Now use one of the pairs of words above in an original sentence.

_____

_____

## 4 Adding Roots to Make Complete Words

Write one of the following roots in each blank below to make a whole word that makes sense in the phrase or sentence. Then write the whole word on the right.

*tain    ten    sign    sort    stance/stant*

**Whole words**

1. a _____ificant event        _____

2. a table of con_____ts       _____

3. an enter_____ing show       _____

4. I re_____ed from my job.    _____

5. circum_____ial evidence     _____

6. an as_____ment of colors    _____

7. She's a fashion de_____er.   _____

8. They traveled a great di_____.   _____

9. The suspects were de_____ed.   _____

10. a dangerous chemical sub_____   _____

## 5 Challenge Word Building

On a separate piece of paper, combine the morphemes below to build as many words as you can. Use as few or as many morphemes as you need for each word. Use a dictionary if you are unsure of a word.

| **Prefixes** | **Roots** | **Suffixes** |
|---|---|---|
| con- | sign | -er |
| de- | sort | -ment |
| re- | tail | |
| | tain | |

## 6 Changing Prefixes

Remove the prefix from each of the words below and replace it with one of the following prefixes. Then use the new word in a phrase or short sentence.

*as-    con-    de-    in-    re-    sub-*

| | **New words** | **Phrases or sentences** |
|---|---|---|
| 1. *re*tain | _____ | _____ |
| 2. *en*sign | _____ | _____ |
| 3. *con*sort | _____ | _____ |
| 4. *in*stance | _____ | _____ |
| 5. *di*stantly | _____ | _____ |
| 6. *en*tailing | _____ | _____ |
| 7. *de*signation | _____ | _____ |

## 7 Missing Links

Add a root from this lesson that will link each pair below to form compound words or phrases. The missing link will form the end of the first word or phrase and the beginning of the second. You can use a root more than once. The number of blanks indicates how many letters are in each missing link. Study the example before you begin.

**Example:**    count to  <u>t</u> <u>e</u> <u>n</u>  -spot

1. stop  __ __ __ __  off

2. screen  __ __ __ __  tube

3. five-and-  __ __ __  fold

4. turn  __ __ __ __  light

5. high  __ __ __ __  language

6. road  __ __ __ __  pilot

*vert, text, tour, vent,* **and** *verb*

# 1 Recognizing Roots

In each group of words below, underline the roots listed on the left.

*vert, verge,*     *turn, bend, incline*
*verse*
          convert          converge          perverse

          diverted          divergent          inversion

          subverting          convergence          conversation


*text*          *weave, construct*

          textile          texture          context          pretext


*tour*          *turn, around*

          tourist          contoured          tournament


*vent*          *come, arrive*

          events          intervention          inventor

          venture          adventurous          preventative


*verb*          *word*

          verb          verbatim          verbose          adverb


# 2 Word Building

Join the morphemes that follow to build whole words. Write the words on the lines provided. Remember to drop the silent *e* if necessary.

1. verb + al + ize _____

2. text + ure + al _____

3. re + verse + al _____

4. per + verse + ion _____

5. pre + vent + ion _____

6. con + vent + ion _____

7. en + tour + age _____

9. con + verge + ent _____

8. di + verse + ify _____

10. vent + ure + some _____

# 3 Jumbled Morphemes

Use the morphemes in each group below to create four different words. Remember to change or drop letters if necessary. Write the words on the lines provided.

1. verge   ly   con   ent   di

_____    _____

_____    _____

2. pre   un   able   vent   ly

_____    _____

_____    _____

3. verse   ir   ible   ly   re

_____    _____

_____    _____

4. vent   ion   al   con   un

_____    _____

_____    _____

5. contro   ial   verse   y   con   ly

_____    _____

_____    _____

## 4 Taking Words Apart

Divide the following words into morphemes and write each one under the correct heading. Remember to add the silent *e* to the root if necessary.

|  | **Prefixes** | **Roots** | **Suffixes** |
|---|---|---|---|
| 1. tourism | | _____ | _____ |
| 2. university | _____ | _____ | _____ |
| 3. invention | _____ | _____ | _____ |
| 4. contextual | _____ | _____ | _____ |
| 5. conversion | _____ | _____ | _____ |
| 6. divergence | _____ | _____ | _____ |
| 7. proverbial | _____ | _____ | _____ |
| 8. eventually | _____ | _____ | _____ _____ |

## 5 Variant Forms

Verbs with the root *vert* often have related words ending in *verse* and *version*. Knowing the *verse* form will help you decide how to spell the /zhən/ at the end of related *version* words. Add the prefixes listed on the left to the roots *vert*, *verse*, and *version* and write the whole words under the correct headings.

|  | **vert** | **verse** | **version** |
|---|---|---|---|
| 1. in- | _____ | _____ | _____ |
| 2. re- | _____ | _____ | _____ |
| 3. di- | _____ | _____ | _____ |
| 4. per- | _____ | _____ | _____ |
| 5. con- | _____ | _____ | _____ |

Say the words in the last column aloud. Notice how they're pronounced. When you hear the ending /zhən/, it is probably spelled *-sion*.

# 6 Adding Roots to Make Complete Words

Write one of the following roots in each blank below to make a whole word.
Remember to drop the silent *e* from the root if necessary. Then use the word in an
original phrase or sentence.

*vert/verge/verse*     *text*     *tour*     *vent*

**Phrases or sentences**

1. con_____s    _____

2. ad_____ity    _____

3. uni_____al    _____

4. in_____ory    _____

5. in_____ion    _____

6. une_____ful    _____

7. di_____ence    _____

8. intro_____ed    _____

# 7 Recognizing Roots in Context

Underline the following roots in the sentences below.

*vert/verse*     *text*     *tour*     *vent*     *verb*

1. I like the new version of the story better.

2. Please don't take my words out of context.

3. The tour of the city was quite an adventure.

4. Isn't there a proverb about too many cooks?

5. The advent of television changed people's lives.

6. Nonverbal communication takes place without words.

7. There are many controversial theories about the universe.

8. A new fabric with the texture of cotton has been invented.

## Roots Presented in This Unit

| | | | |
|---|---|---|---|
| act | mand | prove | tain |
| cent | mend | quer | ten |
| cord | merge | quest | tend |
| cure | merse | quire | tense |
| fact | muse | sane | tent |
| fect | pass | sect | test |
| fic(t) | pat | serve | text |
| file | ply | side | tour |
| fine | pone | sign | vent |
| fit | port | sort | verb |
| found | pose | stance | verge |
| fund | post | stant | verse |
| fuse | pound | tail | vert |

## 1 Recognizing Roots in Context

Underline the roots from the list above in the following sentences.

1. I question how sanitary that canning factory is.

2. The detour diverted us through a residential area.

3. She's learning to conquer her dislike of intense cold.

4. It's our intention to start composting some of our garbage.

5. I'd recommend you wear that new outfit for the interview.

6. In this instance, it's beneficial to have a wide assortment of supplies.

7. The fundamental problem is compounded by the many details involved.

8. His health shows occasional signs of improvement, but the disease is actually incurable.

## 2 Adding Roots to Make Complete Words

Write one of the following roots in each blank below to make a whole word. Remember to change or drop letters if necessary. Then use each word in a phrase or short sentence.

*act   fect   pose   side   stant   tend   verge*

**Phrases or sentences**

1. in_____   _____

2. sup_____   _____

3. _____ive   _____

4. re_____   _____

5. con_____   _____

6. _____ency   _____

7. ef_____   _____

8. com_____   _____

## 3 Practicing Strategies: Words Ending in /shən/

For each word listed below, write a related word that ends in *-ion*. Use the dictionary if necessary.

1. extend _____   6. divert _____

2. intent _____   7. confuse _____

3. revert _____   8. attend _____

4. immerse _____   9. convert _____

5. contend _____   10. pretend _____

Use one pair of words in an original sentence.

_____

_____

## 4 Practicing Strategies: /ənt/, /əns/, and /ənsē/

Several roots in this unit can have the suffixes *-ant/-ance/-ancy* or *-ent/-ence/-ency* added to them. For each root on the left, check the correct column to show which suffixes can be added. Then write an example of the root with one of the suffixes added on the right. Use a dictionary and remember to add, drop, or change letters if necessary. The first one is done for you.

| | -ant/-ance/-ancy | -ent/-ence/-ency | Example words |
|---|---|---|---|
| 1. fine | ✓ | | finance |
| 2. accord | | | |
| 3. disinfect | | | |
| 4. emerge | | | |
| 5. comply | | | |
| 6. compone | | | |
| 7. import | | | |
| 8. preside | | | |
| 9. attend | | | |
| 10. diverge | | | |

## 5 Challenge Word Building

On a separate piece of paper, combine the morphemes below to build as many words as you can. Use as few or as many morphemes as you need for each word. Remember to drop or change letters if necessary. Use a dictionary if you are unsure of a word.

| Prefixes | Roots | Suffixes |
|---|---|---|
| at- | act | -ant/-ance/-ancy |
| pre- | side | -ent/-ence/-ency |
| re- | tend | -ion |
| | tent | |

## 6 Choosing the Correct Form of a Root

To complete the partial words in the following sentences, choose the correct form of the root from those under each blank and write it in the blank. Remember to drop the silent *e* if necessary.

1. That company sup_____es ex_____ion cords.
   <br>          ply/pli          tent/tense

2. His con_____ complaints are a re_____ion to his old habits.
   <br>     stance/stant         vert/verse

3. Are you im_____ing that I'm too lazy to walk that di_____?
   <br>      ply/pli                     stance/stant

4. If your ap_____cation is late, you are in _____ly disqualified.
   <br>      ply/pli             stance/stant

5. I have every in_____ion of com_____ing with the regulations.
   <br>     tent/tense          ply/pli

## 7 Missing Letters

A pair of letters has been omitted twice from each word below. Fill in the missing letters to make whole words. Each word contains a root from this unit.

1. __ __ qui __ __
2. m __ __ nt __ __ n
3. __ __ f __ __ ity
4. __ __ actm __ __ t
5. pr __ __ erv __ __
6. rev __ __ b __ __ ate

7. __ __ vert __ __ g
8. d __ __ erv __ __
9. __ __ def __ __ ite
10. m __ __ g __ __
11. t __ __ d __ __ cy
12. p __ __ v __ __ se

# Greek Roots

### graph, gram, photo, phono, tele, and thermo

## 1 Recognizing Roots

In each group of words below, underline the roots listed on the left.

*graph*          *write, draw*

graphics          telegraph          geography

autograph          autobiography          photographic


*gram*          *write, draw*

grammar          program          diagram

gramophone          telegram          anagram


*photo*          *light*

photocopy          photostat          telephoto

photograph          photosynthesis          unphotogenic


*phono, phone,*          *sound*
*phon*
phonetics          telephone          symphony

phonology          microphone          gramophone


*tele*          *distant*

telegram          telegraph          telephoto

television          telephone          telecommunications


*thermo, therm*          *heat*

thermal          thermostat          isotherm

thermometer          thermonuclear          thermodynamics

## 2 Word Building

Join the morphemes that follow to build whole words. Write the words on the lines provided. Remember to drop the silent *e* if necessary.

1. tele + scope _____

2. tele + path + y _____

3. photo + gen + ic _____

4. re + pro + gram _____

5. geo + therm + al _____

6. photo + copy + er _____

7. stereo + phon + ic _____

8. biblio + graph + er_____

9. gram + mat + ic + al _____

10. demo + graph + ic + s _____

## 3 Greek Roots as Combining Forms

Morphemes from Greek can often be used in more than one way to build words. Some Greek morphemes may be used as a prefix in one word, as a root in another, and as a suffix in a third word. This is why they are sometimes called combining forms.

**Part A.** Write each of the following words under the morphemes they contain.

| telephone | phonograph | telephoto | photograph | telegraph |

| *tele* | *graph* | *photo* | *phono* |
| --- | --- | --- | --- |
| _____ | _____ | _____ | _____ |
| _____ | _____ | _____ | _____ |
| _____ | _____ | | |

**Part B.** Many Greek morphemes end in *o*. Several of these have a variant form without the final *o*. The form that ends in *o* is usually used before a morpheme that starts with a consonant. Underline the form of *phono* used in each word below.

phonograph   phonology   microphone   gramophone

Now say these words aloud. The *o* ending on combining forms is sometimes pronounced as a schwa when the ending is added. Knowing that Greek combining forms usually have an *o* can help you to spell the schwa sound in these words.

## 4 Discovering Patterns: /f/ Spelled *ph*

Underline the words below in which *ph* spells /f/. Then fill in the blank in the pattern.

| | | | |
|---|---|---|---|
| uphill | peephole | apostrophe | photography |
| digraph | philosophy | blasphemy | reupholstered |
| headphone | upheaval | shepherd | autobiographical |

Notice that the words you underlined include Greek roots.

**Pattern:** In words from Greek, the /f/ sound is usually spelled _____.

## 5 Adding Morphemes to Make Complete Words

Write one of the following morphemes in each blank below to make a whole word. The word must make sense in the phrase or sentence. Use a dictionary if necessary. Then write the whole word on the right.

*graph   gram   photo   phone/phon   tele   thermo/therm*

**Whole words**

1. a mono_____med shirt          _____

2. That's a long para_____.          _____

3. an interesting pro_____          _____

4. a talented choreo_____er          _____

5. The debate was _____vised.          _____

6. _____synthesis involves light.          _____

7. Astronomers need _____scopes.          _____

8. She's an excellent saxo_____ist.          _____

9. Please turn the _____stat down.          _____

10. The cheerleader used a mega_____.          _____

# Greek Roots

## *bio, crat, cyclo, log, gen, astro,* and *geo*

## 1 Recognizing Roots

In each group of words below, underline the roots listed on the left.

*bio* — *life*

| | | |
|---|---|---|
| biology | antibiotic | biopsy |
| symbiotic | autobiography | biomedical |

*crat, cracy* — *representative or form of government, power*

| | | |
|---|---|---|
| democrat | bureaucracy | aristocracy |
| democracy | bureaucratic | idiosyncratic |

*cyclo, cycle* — *circle, wheel*

| | | |
|---|---|---|
| cyclone | cycle | recycle |
| bicycling | cyclical | motorcycle |

*log(ue), logy* — *word, speech; study of*

| | | | |
|---|---|---|---|
| logo | dialog(ue) | biology | eulogy |
| logical | catalog(ue) | theology | anthology |

*gen* — *something produced; producer*

| | | |
|---|---|---|
| genetic | generate | oxygen |
| genesis | generation | carcinogenic |

*astro, ast* — *star, constellation*

| | | | |
|---|---|---|---|
| astronaut | astrology | astronomical | asterisk |

*geo* — *earth*

| | | | |
|---|---|---|---|
| geology | geography | geometry | geophysics |

## 2 Word Building

Join the morphemes that follow to build whole words. Write the words on the lines provided. Remember to drop the silent *e* if necessary.

1. eco + logy _____

2. cycle + ist _____

3. mono + log _____

4. auto + cracy _____

5. cyclo + rama _____

6. geo + metr + ic _____

7. bio + graph + er _____

8. astro + phys + ics _____

9. techno + crat + ic _____

10. gen + er + ate + or _____

## 3 Jumbled Morphemes

Use the morphemes in each group below to create three different words. Choose two words from each group and use them in phrases or short sentences.

**Phrases or sentences**

1. cycle   ist   bi   motor

_____       _____

_____       _____

_____

2. log   bio   al   ic   ist   y

_____       _____

_____       _____

_____

3. crat   demo   ic   ly   al   cracy

_____       _____

_____       _____

_____

## 4 Adding Morphemes to Make Complete Words

Write one of the following morphemes in each blank below to make a whole word. The word must make sense in the phrase or sentence. Then write the whole word on the right.

bio    crat    cycle    log/logy    gen    astro    geo

**Whole words**

1. studying _____metry      _____

2. a careful motor_____ist      _____

3. What a bureau_____ic mess!      _____

4. Is that trash _____degradable?      _____

5. Three _____nauts will be trained.      _____

6. The twins are very photo_____ic.      _____

7. a recently discovered carcino_____      _____

8. The treaty banned bio_____ical warfare.      _____

## 5 Looking at Meanings

Add one of the following roots to each partial word below. The word you create must fit the definition on the left. Use a dictionary if necessary.

bio    log/logy    gen    ast    geo

| Definitions | Partial words | Whole words |
|---|---|---|
| 1. allergy producer | aller | _____ |
| 2. study of the earth | logy | _____ |
| 3. star-shaped symbol | erisk | _____ |
| 4. conversation in a play | dia | _____ |
| 5. story of someone's life | graphy | _____ |
| 6. words expressing regret | apo | _____ |

# Lesson 21 Greek Roots

*aero, techno, mechan, metro, psycho,* and *chrono*

## 1 Recognizing Roots

In each group of words below, underline the roots listed on the left.

*aero, aer* — **air, of aircraft**

| | | |
|---|---|---|
| aerobics | aerosol | aerial |
| aerodynamic | aeronautical | aerate |

*techno, techn* — **art, skill, science**

| | | |
|---|---|---|
| technocrat | technical | technician |
| technology | technique | polytechnic |

*mechan* — **machine**

| | | |
|---|---|---|
| mechanical | mechanics | mechanic |
| mechanization | mechanism | mechanistic |

*metro, metr, meter* — **measure**

| | | |
|---|---|---|
| metrical | diameter | geometry |
| metropolitan | kilometer | optometrist |
| symmetrical | centimeter | thermometer |

*psycho, psych* — **mind, soul**

| | | |
|---|---|---|
| psychology | psychopath | psychiatrist |
| psychoanalytical | psychodrama | psychotherapy |

*chrono, chron* — **time**

| | | |
|---|---|---|
| chronometry | chronic | synchronize |
| chronological | chronicle | anachronistic |

## 2 Word Building

Join the morphemes that follow to build whole words. Write the words on the lines provided.

1. psych + ic _____

2. peri + meter _____

3. aero + space _____

4. techn + ique _____

5. mechan + ize _____

6. syn + chron + ism _____

7. un + aer + ate + ed _____

8. a + sym + metr + y _____

9. chrono + metr + ic _____

10. psycho + ana + lyst _____

## 3 Discovering Patterns: *Ch* Spelling /k/ and the Silent *p*

**Part A.** Underline the words below in which *ch* spells /k/.

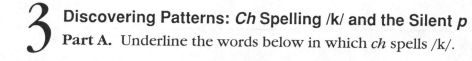

| teacher | French | chronicle | chimney | cherry |
| technicality | psychology | chronology | mechanize | psychoanalysis |

Notice that the words you underlined include Greek roots.

**Pattern:** In words from Greek, the /k/ sound is usually spelled _____.

**Part B.** Look up the pronunciations and origins of the following words, and write the origins on the lines provided.

1. psalm _____

2. pseudo _____

3. pneumatic _____

4. pneumonia _____

**Pattern:** Words from Greek sometimes begin with a silent _____.

**Part C.** Knowing that a word is of Greek origin will usually help you to spell it correctly. Fill in the blanks below.

1. In words from Greek, /f/ is usually spelled _____, and /k/ is usually spelled _____.

2. Words from Greek sometimes begin with a silent _____.

## 4 Taking Words Apart

Divide the following words into morphemes and write one morpheme on each blank.

1. chronic _____ _____

2. geometric _____ _____ _____

3. aerodrome _____ _____

4. technology _____ _____

5. mechanical _____ _____ _____

6. psychopath _____ _____

7. mechanism _____ _____

8. pyrotechnic _____ _____ _____

9. psychologist _____ _____ _____

10. speedometer _____ _____

## 5 Changing Morphemes

Remove the first morpheme from each of the words below and replace it with one of the following morphemes. Then use the word you have created in a phrase or short sentence.

techno/techn      mechan      metr      psycho      chrono

|  | **New words** | **Phrases or sentences** |
|---|---|---|
| 1. *geo*logy | _____ | _____ |
| 2. *psych*ic | _____ | _____ |
| 3. *cycl*ical | _____ | _____ |
| 4. *bio*logical | _____ | _____ |
| 5. *chrono*logist | _____ | _____ |

# 6 Recognizing Morphemes in Context

Underline the following morphemes in the sentences below.

*aero/aer*    *techno*    *mechan*    *metr/meter*    *psycho/psych*    *chrono/chron*

1. Psychedelic drugs affect the mind.

2. A psychopathic killer has a diseased mind.

3. Technophobes fear science and its applications.

4. It has been measured carefully so it's symmetrical.

5. An anachronism places something in the wrong time.

6. Aerating the room helped to bring in some outside air.

7. The aerobatic team did amazing stunts in their airplanes.

8. The new machines led to mechanization and the loss of jobs.

# 7 Double Pyramid

Use the letters found in *aero* to complete the words below. Each word contains the letters *a, e, r,* and *o* at least once in any order. Most of the words are from previous lessons.

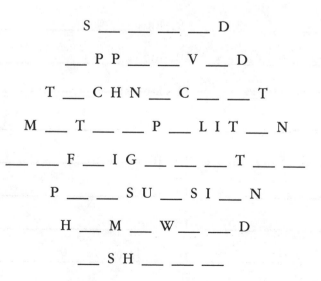

AERO

S __ __ __ __ D

__ P P __ __ V __ D

T __ C H N __ C __ __ T

M __ T __ __ P __ L I T __ N

__ __ F __ I G __ __ __ T __ __

P __ __ S U __ S I __ N

H __ M __ W __ __ D

__ S H __ __ __

## Greek Morphemes Presented in This Unit

| | | | |
|---|---|---|---|
| *aer* | *crat* | *logy* | *photo* |
| *aero* | *cycle* | *mechan* | *psych* |
| *ast* | *cyclo* | *meter* | *psycho* |
| *astro* | *gen* | *metr* | *techn* |
| *bio* | *geo* | *metro* | *techno* |
| *chron* | *gram* | *phon* | *tele* |
| *chrono* | *graph* | *phone* | *therm* |
| *cracy* | *log(ue)* | *phono* | *thermo* |

## 1 Creating Words

Use one of the morphemes above with each of the partial words below to create whole words. Remember to use the form ending in *o,* if there is one, when the next morpheme starts with a consonant. Write the words on the lines provided.

1. bi _____

2. etic _____

3. dia _____

4. demo _____

5. genic _____

6. ic _____

7. ical _____

8. ically _____

9. logy _____

10. logist _____

11. logical _____

12. meter _____

13. pathic _____

14. pro _____

15. tele _____

16. graphy _____

## 2 Looking at Meanings

In the middle column below, write the Greek morphemes that have the meanings listed on the left. Use the glossary if necessary. Then write an example word for each morpheme. The first one is done for you.

| Meanings | Morphemes | Example words |
|---|---|---|
| 1. air, of aircraft | aero | aerosol |
| 2. art, skill, science | | |
| 3. circle, wheel | | |
| 4. distant | | |
| 5. earth | | |
| 6. form of government | | |
| 7. word, speech | | |
| 8. heat | | |
| 9. life | | |
| 10. light | | |
| 11. machine | | |
| 12. measure | | |
| 13. mind | | |
| 14. something produced | | |
| 15. sound | | |
| 16. star | | |
| 17. time | | |
| 18. study of | | |

## 3 Greek Morphemes Ending in *o*

Add the correct form of the morphemes listed on the left to each partial word below. Remember that Greek morphemes ending in *o* are usually used before morphemes beginning with consonants. The forms without the *o* are usually used before morphemes beginning with vowels. Remember to drop the silent *e* if necessary. Write the whole words on the lines provided.

| Roots | Partial words | Whole words |
|---|---|---|
| 1. aero/aer | _____ial | _____ |
| 2. astro/ast | _____naut | _____ |
| 3. cyclo/cycle | _____ist | _____ |
| 4. techno/techn | _____icality | _____ |
| 5. psycho/psych | _____pathic | _____ |
| 6. chrono/chron | _____logical | _____ |
| 7. thermo/therm | _____al | _____ |
| 8. phono/phone/phon | _____etic | _____ |

## 4 Creating Words in Sentences

Combine the morphemes under each blank to create words that make sense in the following sentences.

1. Our last _____ bill was really high.
   phone  tele

2. I like animals and often watch _____ programs.
   ic  log  al  zoo

3. Cigarette smoke is _____ according to that TV _____.
   gen  carcino  ic                                    pro  gram

4. The _____ crew and the _____ were excellent.
   ic  al  techn                              er  graph  s  photo

5. The _____ and Republican parties had productive _____.
   crat  Demo  ic                                              s  log  dia

# 5 Crossword Puzzle

Use the clues below to complete this crossword puzzle. Many of the answers are words with Greek morphemes.

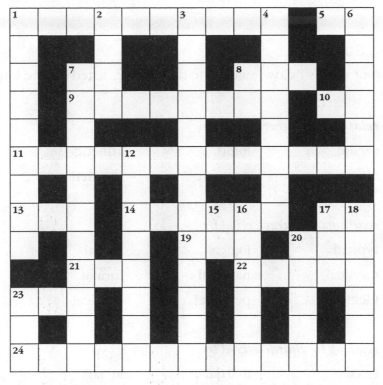

## Across

1. Person who works in a government department
5. "To _____ or not to _____ . . ."
7. Abbreviation for postscript
8. Moved quickly on foot
9. Water is composed of oxygen and _____.
10. Homophone of two
11. One's own life story
13. Large pig
14. Place where clothes are kept
17. He goes with Ma.
19. An empty space
20. I am, you _____, he is
21. _____'s well that ends well.
22. Prefix meaning between or among
23. To knock on a door
24. Having to do with the mind

## Down

1. Story of someone's life
2. Opposite of difficult
3. In the order that things happened in time
4. To carry out business
6. Speech given at a funeral
7. The process of taking and printing pictures
8. Prefix meaning back, again, or anew
12. A sudden backward whipping motion
15. Abbreviation for South America
16. A short section that follows the end of a book or play
17. Prefix meaning before
18. Antenna that brings a radio signal into your car
20. Room at the top of a house
23. Tear roughly

# Suffixes

### *–ic, –al, –ial, –ous,* and *–ious*

## 1 Recognizing Suffixes

In each group of words below, underline the suffixes listed on the left.

*-ic*     *relating to, characterized by*

| | | | |
|---|---|---|---|
| medic | logic | athletic | Hispanic |
| electric | dynamic | magnetic | individualistic |

*-al*     *relating to, characterized by*

| | | | |
|---|---|---|---|
| typical | logical | global | usual |
| medical | national | formal | annual |
| electrical | personal | comical | gradual |

*-ial*     *relating to, characterized by*

| | | | |
|---|---|---|---|
| trivial | martial | racial | especially |
| material | essential | official | perennially |
| memorial | residential | beneficial | confidentially |

*-ous*     *full of, characterized by*

| | | | |
|---|---|---|---|
| nervous | famous | outrageous | generous |
| dangerous | mountainous | advantageous | simultaneous |

*-ious*     *full of, characterized by*

| | | | |
|---|---|---|---|
| curious | infectious | precious | anxiously |
| previous | nutritious | delicious | ferociously |
| mysterious | pretentious | unconscious | conscientious |

## 2 Word Building

Join the morphemes that follow to build whole words. Write the words on the lines provided. Remember to add, drop, or change letters if necessary.

1. glory + ous _____

2. gen + er + ic _____

3. mystery + ous _____

4. nature + al + ly _____

5. ob + nox + ious _____

6. bio + log + ic + al _____

7. hero + ic + al + ly _____

8. im + part + ial + ly _____

9. contro + verse + ial _____

10. mono + tone + ous _____

## 3 Combining Suffixes

Sometimes several suffixes are added to a root at once. The suffixes -*ic*, -*al*, and -*ly* are often combined. Add -*ic*, -*al*, and -*ly* to the partial words below. Write the new words on the lines provided. The first one is done for you.

1. democrat  _democratically_

2. pract _____

3. mechan _____

4. numer _____

5. techn _____

6. crit _____

7. ident _____

8. polit _____

## 4 Adding -*al* to Roots That End in *tu*

When the suffix -*al* is added to roots that end in *tu*, the sound of the *t* changes. Add -*al* to the following roots and write the whole words on the lines provided. Then answer the questions that follow.

1. actu _____

2. factu _____

3. eventu _____

4. mutu _____

5. punctu _____

6. perpetu _____

Pronounce each word you formed. Notice how the endings sound.

When you hear /chuəl/ at the end of a word, how is it usually spelled? _____

# 5 Spelling /shəl/ and /shəs/

When *-ial* and *-ious* follow *c* or *t,* they create spelling problems because both *-cial* and *-tial* spell /shəl/. Likewise, both *-cious* and *-tious* spell /shəs/. The following exercises will give you some related-word strategies for deciding which spelling to use. Check your spellings in a dictionary when necessary.

**Part A.** If a word ends in *ce* and you are adding the suffixes *-ial* or *-ious,* you usually begin the final syllable with the letter *c.* Write a word ending in *ce* for each adjective below.

1. official _____

2. malicious _____

3. vicious _____

4. gracious _____

5. financial _____

6. commercial _____

**Part B.** There are exceptions to this pattern. When adding *-ial* or *-ious* to the following words, you change *ce* to *t.* Add *-ial* or *-ious* to the words below.

1. palace _____

2. essence _____

3. conscience _____

4. substance _____

5. preference _____

6. circumstance _____

**Part C.** If a word ends in *t* and you are adding the suffixes *-ial* or *-ious,* you usually begin the final syllable with the letter *t.* Add *-ial* or *-ious* to the words below. Remember to add, drop, or change letters if necessary.

1. infect _____

2. repeat _____

3. resident _____

4. confident _____

5. different _____

6. consequent _____

Notice that the last four words end in *-ent.* Each of these words also has a form that ends in *-ence.* When there are related words that end in both *-ent* and *-ence,* /shəl/ is nearly always spelled *-tial.*

*Benefit* and *suspect* are exceptions to this strategy for words ending in *t.* Form the words below. Pronounce them first. Then check your spelling in a dictionary.

1. benefit + ial _____

2. suspect + ious _____

# 6 Discovering Patterns: Keeping the Silent *e*

Join the morphemes below to build whole words. Write the words on the lines provided. Check your spelling in a dictionary.

1. gorge + ous _____     3. cour + age + ous _____

2. out + rage + ous _____     4. ad + vant + age + ous _____

Notice that the silent *e* is not dropped when *-ous* is added to these words. How does the silent *e* affect the way the *g* is pronounced in the words you built?

_____

# 7 Another Related-Word Strategy

Some nouns ending in *-tion* can be made into adjectives by changing *-tion* to *-tious*. Change the nouns below to adjectives. Then complete the sentences by using the appropriate form of each word.

| Nouns | Adjectives ending in *-ious* | Sentences |
|---|---|---|
| 1. nutrition | _____ | It is a _____ cereal. |
| 2. caution | _____ | Please proceed with _____. |
| 3. ambition | _____ | His _____ will take him a long way. |
| 4. flirtation | _____ | She has a _____ manner. |
| 5. infection | _____ | How long did the _____ last? |
| 6. superstition | _____ | I am _____ about black cats. |

**Strategy:** If a noun that ends in *-tion* has a related word that ends in /shəs/, the ending will be spelled *-tious*.

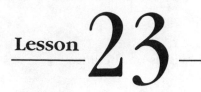

# Suffixes

### –age, –ate, –ite, –able, and –ible

## 1 Recognizing Suffixes

In each group of words below, underline the suffixes listed on the left.

**-age**  *action or result of an action; collection; state*

| | | | |
|---|---|---|---|
| damage | usage | postage | shortage |
| blockage | message | language | breakage |

**-ate**  *cause, make;*     *state, condition;*   *someone who*

| | | | |
|---|---|---|---|
| evaluate | activate | fortunate | associate |
| stimulate | decorate | desperate | candidate |

**-ite**  *quality of; follower or resident of;*     *mineral product*

| | | | |
|---|---|---|---|
| infinite | favorite | Israelite | granite |
| definite | opposite | Mennonite | graphite |

**-able**  *able to, capable of, liable to*

| | | | |
|---|---|---|---|
| adorable | tolerable | profitable | flammable |
| considerable | dependable | comfortable | remarkable |

**-ible**  *able to, capable of, liable to*

| | | | |
|---|---|---|---|
| terrible | eligible | incredible | horrible |
| possible | sensible | comprehensible | invisible |

## 2 Word Building

Join the morphemes that follow to build whole words. Write the words on the lines provided. Remember to change or drop letters if necessary.

1. rely + able _____

2. gradu + ate _____

3. dis + pose + able _____

4. ir + re + sist + ible _____

5. dynam + ite _____     8. dis + ad + vant + age _____

6. en + cour + age _____     9. in + ex + cuse + able _____

7. de + duct + ible _____     10. in + vite + ate + ion _____

## 3 Combining Suffixes

Sometimes two suffixes are used together to form words. The suffixes *-ate* and *-ion* are often combined. Add *-ate* and *-ion* to the roots below. Remember to add, drop, or change letters if necessary.

1. adapt _____     5. inform _____

2. expire _____     6. explore _____

3. install _____     7. concentr _____

4. qualify _____     8. determine _____

## 4 Related-Word Strategy: Words that End in /əbl/

Pronounce the words in Exercise 1 that end in *-able* and *-ible* and listen to the sounds of the endings. Because the suffixes *-able* and *-ible* sound alike, even very good spellers often have to check the spelling of these suffixes in the dictionary. There are a few strategies to help you predict these spellings, however.

**Strategy:** Many words that end in /əbl/ have a related word that ends in /shən/ or /āshən/. If you can hear a long *a* before the /shən/, the related word will probably end in *-able*.

Following this strategy, write a word ending in *-able* or *-ible* for each of the words below. Use a dictionary if necessary. The first one is done for you.

1. division ___divisible___     6. adaptation _____

2. digestion _____     7. destruction _____

3. collection _____     8. conversion _____

4. separation _____     9. application _____

5. admiration _____     10. imagination _____

# 5 Using Probabilities to Predict the Spelling of /əbl/

There are two other strategies to use in predicting the spelling of /əbl/.

**Strategy 1:** There are four words with the suffix *-able* for every word that has the suffix *-ible*. So if you have to guess how to spell a word that ends in /əbl/, you should probably guess *-able*.

**Strategy 2:** If the root ends in a soft *c* or *g*, the suffix *-ible* is probably added to keep the /s/ or /j/ sound of the root.

Add *-able* or *-ible* to the roots below using these two strategies. Remember to change or drop letters if necessary. Use a dictionary if you are unsure of a spelling.

1. like _____
2. avail _____
3. move _____
4. break _____
5. inelig _____

6. force _____
7. neglig _____
8. applic _____
9. invince _____
10. reproduce _____

# 6 Using the Dictionary

A few words don't follow Strategy 2 above. Look up the /əbl/ form of each word below and write it on the line provided. Then answer the question that follows.

1. notice _____
2. change _____
3. service _____
4. enforce _____
5. replace _____
6. manage _____

7. trace _____
8. peace _____
9. charge _____
10. salvage _____
11. marriage _____
12. knowledge _____

Notice that the silent *e* is not dropped when *-able* is added to these words. What does the silent *e* do in these words?

_____

# 7 The Suffixes -ate and -ite

When the suffixes -ate and -ite are unaccented, they sound alike. Pronounce the words below and listen for the sound of the last syllable.

> desperate     fortunate     definite     favorite

In many words, you can hear the sound of the vowel in these suffixes. When the vowel sound is a schwa, however, the best strategy is to use a dictionary if you are unsure of a spelling. Add -ate or -ite to the roots below and write the words on the lines provided.

1. delic _____

2. oppos _____

3. obstin _____

4. exquis _____

5. legitim _____

6. inaccur _____

7. compos _____

8. affection _____

# 8 Recognizing Suffixes in Context

Underline the following suffixes in the sentences below.

> -age     -ate     -ite     -able     -ible

1. Is it possible to fix the damaged bicycle?

2. Chocolate is definitely my favorite flavor.

3. My uncle says cultivating vegetables is enjoyable.

4. Did you get the message that your package had arrived?

5. This fabric is durable, comfortable, and almost indestructible.

6. The most affordable residential area is isolated from the shops.

7. Despite his incredible appetite, he manages to keep in shape.

8. I participated in the tournament but was eliminated right away.

9. One of the advantages of our car is that it gets good gas mileage.

10. The salesperson encouraged us to buy a very adaptable piece of furniture.

# Suffixes

*–ist, –ism, –ive, –ize, and –ine*

## 1 Recognizing Suffixes

In each group of words below, underline the suffixes listed on the left.

**-ist**        *someone who*

| | | | |
|---|---|---|---|
| artist | racist | tourist | optimist |
| scientist | realist | motorist | idealistic |

**-ism**        *act, condition, doctrine, or practice of*

| | | | |
|---|---|---|---|
| racism | capitalism | hypnotism | Judaism |
| realism | patriotism | alcoholism | communism |

**-ive**        *performing or tending toward an action*

| | | | |
|---|---|---|---|
| addictive | expensive | festive | selective |
| distinctive | constructive | cooperative | progressive |

**-ize**        *cause to be or become*

| | | | |
|---|---|---|---|
| civilize | finalize | terrorize | equalize |
| criticize | organize | apologize | mechanize |

**-ine**        *of, pertaining to;*        *chemical substance*

| | | |
|---|---|---|
| famine | routine | chlorine |
| feminine | medicine | antihistamine |

## 2 Word Building

Join the morphemes that follow to build whole words. Write the words on the lines provided. Remember to drop the silent *e* if necessary.

1. div + ine _____    3. pessim + ist _____

2. genu + ine _____    4. familiar + ize _____

5. art + ist + ic _____

6. penal + ize _____

7. social + ism _____

8. altern + ate + ive _____

9. imagin + ate + ive _____

10. in + con + clus + ive _____

 **Combining Suffixes**

Sometimes several suffixes are added to a root at once. The suffixes *-ize, -ate,* and *-ion* are often combined. Add *-ize, -ate,* and *-ion* to the roots below. Write the new words on the lines provided. Remember to add, drop, or change letters if necessary.

1. civil _____

2. final _____

3. organ _____

4. brutal _____

5. fertile _____

6. central _____

7. modern _____

8. dramat _____

9. hospital _____

10. alphabet _____

 **Creating and Using Words**

For each root listed below, create two different words by adding two of the following suffixes. Then use each word you form in a phrase or short sentence.

|  | *-ist* | *-ism* | *-ize* |
|---|---|---|---|

| | **New words** | **Phrases or sentences** |
|---|---|---|
| 1. ideal | _____ | _____ |
| | _____ | _____ |
| 2. critic | _____ | _____ |
| | _____ | _____ |
| 3. optim | _____ | _____ |
| | _____ | _____ |

## 5 Completing Words in Sentences

Add one of the following suffixes to the root listed under each blank below and write the completed word in the blank. The word must make sense in the sentence. Use a dictionary if necessary.

-ist    -ism    -ive    -ize    -ine

1. Her grandson is an _____ and _____ child.
                                 act                          aggress

2. I _____ that the treatment will be _____.
               recogn                           expens

3. The _____ was angry about the _____ of her work.
              scient                       critic

4. The new _____ attraction gave a boost to _____ in the area.
                 tour                       tour

5. The doctor will _____ her and prescribe some _____ for her.
                 exam                    medic

## 6 Missing Morphemes

One of the suffixes from this lesson can be added to every root in each group below. Fill in the missing suffixes to make whole words. Use a different suffix for each group.

1. national_____    solo_____    cycl_____    pessim_____    extrem_____

2. pessim_____    hero_____    national_____    extrem_____    vandal_____

3. furt_____    creat_____    attent_____    intens_____    effect_____

4. vandal_____    national_____    hospital_____    categor_____    glamor_____

## 1 Recognizing Suffixes

In each group of words below, underline the suffixes listed on the left.

*-ure*          *act, process; function or body performing a function*

| | | | |
|---|---|---|---|
| measure | nature | adventure | failure |
| exposure | picture | agriculture | legislature |

*-y*          *characterized by*

| | | | |
|---|---|---|---|
| shiny | dirty | funny | agony |
| cloudy | rainy | healthy | remedy |

*-ty, -ity*          *state or quality of*

| | | | |
|---|---|---|---|
| loyalty | certainty | quality | maturity |
| honesty | availability | festivity | inactivity |

*-ice*          *state or quality of*

| | | | |
|---|---|---|---|
| justice | notice | novice | malice |
| service | prejudice | practice | malicious |

## 2 Word Building

Join the morphemes that follow to build whole words. Write the words on the lines provided. Remember to add, drop, or change letters if necessary.

1. thirst + y _____

2. fidel + ity _____

3. cult + ure _____

4. fract + ure _____

5. difficul + ty _____

6. un + health + y _____

7. im + moral + ity _____

8. serv + ice + able _____

9. mal + pract + ice _____

10. dis + please + ure _____

## 3  Changing the Function of Words

Many suffixes change the way words are used. Adding -ize to words can change them to verbs. The suffixes -y or -ity can change words to nouns. For each root below, write a verb ending in -ize and a noun ending in -y or -ity. Remember to drop the silent e if necessary. The first one is done for you.

| Roots | Verbs ending in -ize | Nouns ending in -y or -ity |
|-------|----------------------|-----------------------------|
| 1. agon | agonize | agony |
| 2. fertile | | |
| 3. apolog | | |
| 4. mobile | | |
| 5. special | | |
| 6. harmon | | |
| 7. national | | |
| 8. personal | | |

Use one pair of words that you formed in original sentences.

_____

_____

## 4  Adding -ure to Roots That End in s or t

When the suffix -ure follows s or t, the sounds of the s and t change. Add -ure to the following roots and write the whole words on the lines provided. Then pronounce each whole word and notice the sound of the ending.

1. nat _____     5. treas _____

2. fut _____     6. depart _____

3. leis _____    7. pleas _____

4. meas _____    8. struct _____

## 5 Alternative Spellings for /chər/

Pronounce the words below and notice how the endings sound.

picture          pitcher

1. What suffix was added to the root *pict?*  _____

2. What suffix was added to the root *pitch?*  _____

When *-ure* is added to a root that ends in *t,* it sounds the same as when *-er* is added to a word that ends in *ch.* Remove the suffixes from the words below and write the roots on the lines provided.

1. catcher _____

2. teacher _____

3. searcher _____

4. stretcher _____

5. feature _____

6. creature _____

7. miniature _____

8. manufacture _____

Look at the roots and fill in the blanks in the pattern below.

**Pattern:** For words that end in /chər/, if the root is a whole word that ends in *-ch,* the suffix will be spelled _____.

When the root is not a whole word, the suffix will be spelled _____.

## 6 Recognizing Suffixes in Context

Underline the following suffixes in the sentences below.

*-ure*    *-y*    *-ty*    *-ity*    *-ice*

1. My daughter's room is dusty and messy.

2. He practiced those gestures until they looked natural.

3. She has the ability to solve a problem of this complexity.

4. That is a dangerous activity, and failure could result in their death.

5. Do you know the pledge that ends "with liberty and justice for all"?

6. The vice president's signature will grant the authority to order that service.

**7 Taking Words Apart**

Divide the following words into morphemes and write each one under the correct heading.

|  | Prefixes | Roots | Suffixes |
|---|---|---|---|
| 1. gesture | | _____ | _____ |
| 2. maturity | | _____ | _____ _____ |
| 3. humanity | | _____ | _____ |
| 4. exposure | _____ | _____ | _____ |
| 5. unworthy | _____ | _____ | _____ |
| 6. apprentice | _____ | _____ | _____ |

**8 Creating and Using Adjectives**

Adding the suffix -*y* can change a noun to an adjective. Choose five of the following nouns and change them to adjectives by adding -*y*. Note that the suffix -*y* is considered a vowel, so the silent *e* is dropped when the suffix -*y* is added. Then use each adjective in an original phrase or sentence. One is done for you.

| dirt | fish | sleep | taste | storm |
|---|---|---|---|---|
| grass | greed | shade | hand | wealth |

| | Adjectives | Phrases or sentences |
|---|---|---|
| 1. | dirty | a very dirty car |
| 2. | _____ | _____ |
| 3. | _____ | _____ |
| 4. | _____ | _____ |
| 5. | _____ | _____ |
| 6. | _____ | _____ |

## Suffixes Presented in This Unit

| -able | -ible | -ism | -ize |
|-------|-------|------|------|
| -age  | -ic   | -ist | -ous |
| -al   | -ice  | -ite | -ty  |
| -ate  | -ine  | -ity | -ure |
| -ial  | -ious | -ive | -y   |

**1** **Taking Words Apart**

Divide the following words into morphemes and write one on each blank.

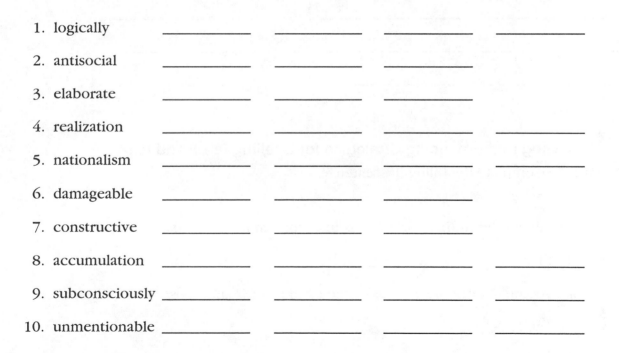

1. logically _____ _____ _____ _____

2. antisocial _____ _____ _____

3. elaborate _____ _____ _____

4. realization _____ _____ _____ _____

5. nationalism _____ _____ _____ _____

6. damageable _____ _____ _____

7. constructive _____ _____ _____

8. accumulation _____ _____ _____ _____

9. subconsciously _____ _____ _____ _____

10. unmentionable _____ _____ _____ _____

## 2 Reviewing and Practicing Strategies for Spelling /əbl/

**Part A.** Complete the following sentences.

1. The most common spelling of /əbl/ is _____.

2. If there is a related word ending in -*ation*, /əbl/ is usually spelled _____.

3. To keep a *c* or a *g* soft at the end of a root, /əbl/ is usually spelled _____.

4. Sometimes the silent *e* is kept to keep a *c* or a *g* soft when _____ is added.

**Part B.** Add -*able* or -*ible* to the roots below and write the whole words in the correct column. Check your spelling in a dictionary if necessary.

| | | |
|---|---|---|
| ador | comprehens | excuse | indestruct | poss | transport |
| believe | elig | notice | knowledge | profit | value |

**-able**         **-able**        **-ible**

_____    _____    _____

_____    _____    _____

_____    _____    _____

_____    _____    _____

## 3 Reviewing and Practicing Strategies for Spelling /shəl/ and /shəs/

**Part A.** Complete the following sentences.

1. If you are adding the suffixes -*ial* or -*ious* to a word ending in *ce*, /shəl/ and /shəs/ are

   usually spelled _____ and _____.

2. If you are adding -*ial* or -*ious* to a word ending in *t*, /shəl/ and /shəs/ are usually spelled

   _____ and _____.

3. When there are related words that end in both -*ent* and -*ence*, /shəl/ is usually spelled

   _____.

4. Some nouns ending in -*tion* can be made into adjectives by changing the -*tion* to

   _____.

**Part B.** Add *-ial* or *-ious* to each of the words below. Say the word aloud before you write it. Remember to add, drop, or change letters if necessary.

1. race _____

2. part _____

3. grace _____

4. infect _____

5. malice _____

6. caution _____

7. artifice _____

8. residence _____

9. province _____

10. confident _____

11. suspicion _____

12. ambition _____

## 4 Changing the Meaning of Words

Add the suffixes *-ism, -ist,* and *-ize* to the roots below and write the words in the correct columns.

|  | -ism | -ist | -ize |
|---|---|---|---|
| 1. real | _____ | _____ | _____ |
| 2. terror | _____ | _____ | _____ |
| 3. social | _____ | _____ | _____ |
| 4. plagiar | _____ | _____ | _____ |
| 5. national | _____ | _____ | _____ |

Notice how adding different suffixes changes the meaning of a word. Now use all three forms of two of the above roots in original sentences.

_____

_____

_____

_____

_____

_____

## 5 Challenge Word Building

On a separate piece of paper, combine the morphemes below to build at least 15 words. Use as few or as many parts as you need for each word. Use a dictionary if you are unsure of a word.

| Prefixes | Roots | Suffixes |
|----------|-------|----------|
| af- | fect | -able |
| de- | fine | -ate |
| dis- | pose | -ion |
| in- | | -ite |
| re- | | -ity |
| | | -ive |

## 6 Missing Letters

A pair of letters has been omitted twice from each word below. Fill in the missing letters to make whole words. All of the words contain suffixes from Unit 6.

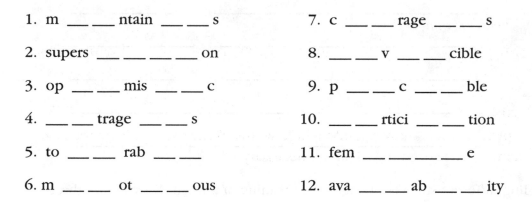

1. m __ __ ntain __ __ s

2. supers __ __ __ __ on

3. op __ __ mis __ __ c

4. __ __ trage __ __ s

5. to __ __ rab __ __

6. m __ __ ot __ __ ous

7. c __ __ rage __ __ s

8. __ __ v __ __ cible

9. p __ __ c __ __ ble

10. __ __ rtici __ __ tion

11. fem __ __ __ __ e

12. ava __ __ ab __ __ ity

116    Unit 6 Review

# Prefixes

## *ob–, anti–, contra–,* and *inter–*

## 1 Recognizing Prefixes

In each group of words below, underline the prefixes listed on the left.

*ob-, oc-,*
*of-, op-*
    *toward; against*

| | | | |
|---|---|---|---|
| obtain | obvious | occur | offensive |
| observe | obstruction | occupy | opposite |

*anti-*
    *against, opposing*

| | | | |
|---|---|---|---|
| antibiotic | antiseptic | antisocial | antifreeze |

*contra-*
    *against*

| | | | |
|---|---|---|---|
| contrast | contradiction | contravene | contraband |

*inter-*
    *between, among*

| | | | |
|---|---|---|---|
| interrupt | intervention | interview | international |

## 2 Word Building

Join the morphemes that follow to build whole words. Write the words on the lines provided. Remember to drop the silent *e* if necessary.

1. anti + trust _____

2. inter + fere_____

3. of + fer + ing _____

4. ob + lige + ed _____

5. inter + rog + ate _____

6. inter + miss + ion _____

7. anti + climac + tic _____

8. oc + cas + ion + al _____

9. contra + cept + ion _____

10. un + ob + trus + ive _____

# 3 Looking at Meanings: *inter-*, *intra-*, and *intro-*; *anti-* and *ante-*

**Part A.** The prefix *inter-* sounds almost like the less common prefixes *intra-* and *intro-*. Knowing their meanings can help you tell them apart. *Intra-* means *inside* or *within*, and *intro-* means *in* or *inward*. Add one of these prefixes to each partial word below to form a word that matches the definition given. Use a dictionary if necessary. The first one is done for you.

|            | *inter-*     | *intra-*  | *intro-*   |
|------------|--------------|-----------|------------|

| Definitions | Partial words | Whole words |
|-------------|---------------|-------------|
| 1. between states | state | interstate |
| 2. within a state | state | |
| 3. lead in | duce | |
| 4. within a city | city | |
| 5. between cities | city | |
| 6. looking inward | spection | |

**Part B.** The prefix *anti-* sounds like a less common prefix, *ante-*, which means *before*. Knowing their different meanings can help you to spell them correctly. List each word below on the line that follows its definition.

| antiwar | antisocial | anteroom |
|---------|------------|----------|
| anterior | antebellum | antidepressant |

| Definitions | Matching words |
|-------------|----------------|
| 1. unsociable, against society | |
| 2. before a war | |
| 3. against war | |
| 4. opposes depression | |
| 5. outer room leading to another | |
| 6. situated before, to the front | |

## 4 Recognizing Patterns: More Prefixes That Change

A few prefixes change when added to roots that begin with certain letters. Remember that these changes often account for double consonants near the beginning of words.

### The Prefix *ob-*

| Prefix | Changes to | Before | Examples |
|--------|-----------|--------|----------|
| ob- | oc- | c | ob + casion = occasion |
| ob- | of- | f | ob + fend = offend |
| ob- | op- | p | ob + portunity = opportunity |

Join the morphemes below, changing *ob-* if necessary.

1. ob + fer _____

2. ob + ponent _____

3. ob + jection _____

4. ob + fensive _____

5. ob + ligatory _____

6. ob + position _____

7. ob + casional _____

8. ob + currence _____

## 5 Changing Prefixes

Remove a prefix from each of the words below and replace it with one of the following prefixes. Then use the word you have created in a phrase or short sentence.

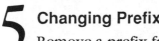

| | New words | Phrases or sentences |
|---|-----------|---------------------|
| 1. *re*ject | _____ | _____ |
| 2. *pre*dict | _____ | _____ |
| 3. *re*marry | _____ | _____ |
| 4. *de*fensive | _____ | _____ |
| 5. *sup*position | _____ | _____ |

# Lesson 27      Prefixes

*auto-, sub-, super-, and trans-*

## 1 Recognizing Prefixes

In each group of words below, underline the prefixes listed on the left.

*auto-, aut-*     *self*

| | | |
|---|---|---|
| autograph | automation | autism |
| automobile | autobiography | autopsy |

*sub-, sup-,*     *under; lesser*
*suc-, suf-*

| | | | |
|---|---|---|---|
| submit | subway | support | success |
| substandard | subconscious | supposed | suffering |

*super-, sur-*     *superior, above; additional*

| | | |
|---|---|---|
| supervisor | superior | survivor |
| supermarket | superficial | surcharge |

*trans-*     *across*

| | | |
|---|---|---|
| transfer | transition | translator |
| transportation | transatlantic | transaction |

## 2 Word Building

Join the morphemes that follow to build whole words. Write the words on the lines provided. Remember to add, drop, or change letters if necessary.

1. auto + crat _____
2. sup + ply + er _____
3. re + sur + face _____
4. sub + mar + ine _____
5. sub + norm + al _____

6. super + flu + ous _____
7. super + stit + ion _____
8. trans + fuse + ion _____
9. auto + nom + ous _____
10. sub + di + vise + ion _____

## 3  Using the Dictionary

Create a whole word starting with each prefix below. Do not use words included in Exercises 1 or 2. Use a dictionary if necessary. Then write a short phrase or sentence using your word.

| | Words | Phrases or sentences |
|---|---|---|
| 1. auto- | _____ | _____ |
| 2. sub- | _____ | _____ |
| 3. super- | _____ | _____ |
| 4. trans- | _____ | _____ |

## 4  Recognizing Patterns: More Prefixes That Change

A few prefixes change when added to roots that begin with certain letters. Remember that these changes often account for double consonants near the beginning of words.

### The Prefix *sub-*

| Prefix | Changes to | Before | Examples |
|---|---|---|---|
| sub- | suc- | c | sub + ceed = succeed |
| sub- | suf- | f | sub + ficient = sufficient |
| sub- | sup- | p | sub + ply = supply |

Join the morphemes below, changing *sub-* if necessary.

1. sub + fix _____

2. sub + text _____

3. sub + focate _____

4. sub + posed _____

5. sub + plier _____

6. sub + cessful _____

7. sub + cession _____

8. sub + stantial _____

Use two of the words you formed in original sentences.

_____

_____

## 5 Looking at Meanings

Add one of the following prefixes to each partial word below to form a word that matches the definition given. Use a dictionary if necessary.

*auto-  sub-  super-  trans-*

| Definitions | Partial words | Whole words |
|---|---|---|
| 1. can be carried across | portable | _____ |
| 2. below the main heading | heading | _____ |
| 3. superior to people | human | _____ |
| 4. self-operating | matic | _____ |
| 5. plunge under | merge | _____ |
| 6. oversee | vise | _____ |
| 7. move over to a new place | plant | _____ |
| 8. self-governing | nomous | _____ |

## 6 Recognizing Prefixes in Context

Underline the following prefixes in the sentences below.

*auto-  sub-  suf-  sup-  super-  sur-  trans-*

1. Many suffragists were subjected to ridicule.

2. The superhighway construction involved several surveyors.

3. The supervisor was so supportive, it was a real transformation.

4. When I'm surrounded by people, I feel as though I'm suffocating.

5. It's not surprising that she automatically suppressed the bad news.

6. Ramón is supposed to get his automobile's transmission overhauled.

# Prefixes

*multi–, poly–, mono–, uni–, bi–, and tri–*

## 1 Recognizing Prefixes

In each group of words below, underline the prefixes listed on the left.

| *multi-* | *much, many* | | |
|---|---|---|---|
| | multiply | multitude | multicultural | multipurpose |

| *poly-* | *much, many* | | |
|---|---|---|---|
| | polyester | polygamy | polytechnic | polyunsaturated |

| *mono-, mon-* | *one, alone* | | |
|---|---|---|---|
| | monopoly | monotonous | monorail | monogram |

| *uni-* | *one* | | |
|---|---|---|---|
| | uniform | united | unique | universe |

| *bi-* | *two* | | |
|---|---|---|---|
| | bicycle | bisect | biweekly | bifocal |

| *tri-* | *three* | | |
|---|---|---|---|
| | triple | triangle | tripod | triathlon |

## 2 Word Building

Join the morphemes that follow to build whole words. Write the words on the lines provided. Remember to drop the silent *e* if necessary.

1. uni + son _____

2. bi + ceps _____

3. tri + plane _____

4. multi + race + ial _____

5. poly + syllab + ic _____

6. mono + pol + ize _____

7. mono + log _____     9. multi + lingu + al _____

8. mon + arch _____     10. bi + cent + enn + ial _____

## 3  Adding Prefixes to Make Complete Words

Each sentence below contains a clue to the meaning of the missing prefix. Write one of the following prefixes in each blank to build a word that makes sense in the sentence. Write the whole words on the lines provided. Then underline the word or words that were the clue.

*poly-*     *mon-*     *uni-*     *bi-*     *tri-*

**Whole words**

1. A _____angle has three sides.                    _____

2. The _____corn has one horn.                      _____

3. The _____gamist had two wives.                   _____

4. In a _____archy, there's one ruler.              _____

5. A _____mester is three months long.              _____

6. A _____graph measures many things.               _____

7. An eyeglass for one eye is a _____ocle.          _____

8. A _____lingual person speaks two languages.  _____

## 4  Jumbled Morphemes

Use the morphemes in each group below to create three different words. Choose two words from each group and use them in short phrases or sentences.

**Phrases or sentences**

1. cycle   tri   bi   uni   ist

_____          _____

_____          _____

_____

2. ous   tonc   mono   ly   y

_____         _____

_____         _____

_____

3. nat   al   multi   ion   ply

_____         _____

_____         _____

_____

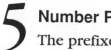

## 5 Number Prefixes

The prefixes in this lesson refer to numbers, either specifically (*uni-, bi-, tri-,* and *mono-*) or in general (*multi-* and *poly-*). Some other number prefixes are listed below. Use a dictionary or math text to find out their meanings, and fill in the blanks. Then write one word starting with each prefix. The first one is done for you.

| Prefix | How many? | Whole words |
|---|---|---|
| 1. quadr | four | quadruple |
| 2. penta | | |
| 3. hexa | | |
| 4. oct | | |
| 5. nona | | |
| 6. deca | | |
| 7. kilo | | |
| 8. mega | | |

Now use two of your words in original sentences.

_____

_____

# Review

## *Prefixes Presented in This Unit* ............................................

| | | | |
|---|---|---|---|
| anti- | mon- | op- | super- |
| aut- | mono- | poly- | sur- |
| auto- | multi- | sub- | trans- |
| bi- | ob- | suc- | tri- |
| contra- | oc- | suf- | uni- |
| inter- | of- | sup- | |

## 1 Taking Words Apart

Divide the following words into morphemes and write each one under the correct heading. You may write either the original form of the prefix or the one used in the word. Remember to add or change letters if necessary.

| | Prefixes | Roots | Suffixes |
|---|---|---|---|
| 1. obscurity | _____ | _____ | _____ |
| 2. opponent | _____ | _____ | _____ |
| 3. bimonthly | _____ | _____ | _____ |
| 4. monotony | _____ | _____ | _____ |
| 5. obligation | _____ | _____ | _____ _____ |
| 6. interracial | _____ | _____ | _____ |
| 7. supporter | _____ | _____ | _____ |
| 8. presuppose | _____ _____ | _____ | |
| 9. subscription | _____ | _____ | _____ |
| 10. contradictory | _____ | _____ | _____ |

## 2 Reviewing Prefixes That Change

**Part A.** Fill in the blanks in the chart below.

| Prefix | Changes to | Before | Example words |
|--------|-----------|--------|---------------|
| ob- | oc- | | |
| | of- | f | |
| ob- | | p | |
| sub- | | c | |
| sub- | suf- | | |
| | sup- | p | |

**Part B.** Write the correct form of the prefixes *ob-* or *sub-* in each blank in the following words. The words must make sense in the sentences.

1. Did you _____cumb to that flu virus?

2. She _____tained the necessary papers.

3. No one _____jected to my leaving early.

4. Prefixes and _____fixes are morphemes.

5. He was _____jected to a full interrogation.

6. The news was _____pressed during the war.

7. The heat and humidity are quite _____pressive.

8. The apartment is _____cupied by a family of eight.

## 3 Changing Prefixes

Remove the prefix from each of the words below and replace it with one of the following prefixes to form a new word.

   *ante-*     *anti-*     *contra-*     *inter-*     *intro-*

1. *sym*biotic _____

2. *ad*diction _____

3. *sub*mission _____

4. *review* _____

5. *post*date _____

6. *pro*duced _____

Now use two of your words in original sentences.

_____

_____

## 4 Adding Prefixes to Roots

Different prefixes can be used with the same root. If the prefix listed at the top of the column can be used with the root on the left, write the word in the correct space. Check a dictionary if necessary. The first one is done for you.

|  | trans- | ob-/of-/op- | sub-/suf-/sup- |
|---|---|---|---|
| 1. press | _____ | oppress | suppress |
| 2. fer | _____ | _____ | _____ |
| 3. fice | _____ | _____ | _____ |
| 4. ject | _____ | _____ | _____ |
| 5. port | _____ | _____ | _____ |
| 6. verse | _____ | _____ | _____ |

## 5 Creating Words in Sentences

Combine the morphemes under each blank to create words that make sense in the following sentences.

1. They hold _____ meetings _____.
   nat inter al ion                          ann bi ly ual

2. He's _____ about not wearing _____.
   stin ate ob                                    form s uni

3. I'm _____ we don't need _____ in the car yet.
   ed prise sur                              freeze anti

4. Her _____ after that _____ accident is miraculous.
   vive al sur                          mobile auto

5. Those curtains are so _____ they're almost _____.
   ial stant sub in                              ent trans par

# 6 Crossword Puzzle

Use the clues below to complete this crossword puzzle. Many of the answers contain prefixes from Unit 7.

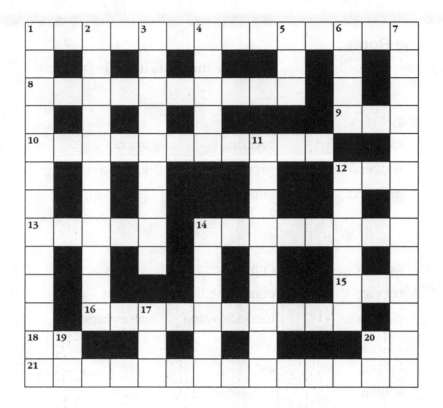

## Across

1. Means of traveling from place to place
8. Having to do with cars
9. A friendly squeeze
10. Of a quality below accepted measures; inferior
12. Steal from
13. Language that provided English with many morphemes
14. A person who manufactures things
15. Also
16. A person or thing that takes the place of another
18. He, she, or _____
20. Short for advertisement
21. Inconsistencies: That statement is full of _____.

## Down

1. Across the ocean between America and Europe
2. Medicines that fight infections
3. Opposite of nothing
4. Many times
5. Consumed food
6. One-twelfth of a foot
7. Residential parts of a town or city
11. Able to operate by itself
12. Say out loud from memory
14. Put up in a public place: The notice was _____ on the bulletin board.
17. To block the way; prevent
19. Opposite of from
20. _____ apple a day

# Roots

*ceed, ceive, cide,* and *clude*

## 1 Recognizing Roots

In each group of words below, underline the roots listed on the left.

*ceed/cede,*
*cess*

go

| | | |
|---|---|---|
| exceed | recede | access |
| succeed | precede | excessive |
| proceed | concede | procession |

*ceive, cept*

take

| | | | |
|---|---|---|---|
| deceive | conceive | accept | receptive |
| receive | conceptual | except | deception |
| perceive | inconceivable | acceptance | perception |

*cide, cise*

kill;                    cut

| | | |
|---|---|---|
| suicide | precise | incision |
| homicide | concise | excised |
| insecticide | decisive | imprecision |

*clude, clus*

close, shut

| | | |
|---|---|---|
| include | exclude | seclusion |
| conclude | preclude | reclusive |

## 2 Word Building

Join the morphemes that follow to build whole words. Write the words on the lines provided. Remember to drop the silent *e* if necessary.

1. pesti + cide _____

2. ne + cess + ity _____

3. pre + cise + ly _____

4. in + cess + ant _____

5. de + ceive + ing _____

6. ante + cede + ent _____

7. ac + cess + ible _____     9. in + con + clus + ive _____

8. se + clude + ed _____     10. mis + con + cept + ion _____

# 3 Variant Forms

All the roots in this lesson have more than one form. The meaning of the roots doesn't change, even when the spelling and pronunciation do. Learning to recognize variant forms of roots can help you to develop spelling strategies.

**Part A.** Words with the root *ceed/cede, ceive,* and *clude* often have related words with the roots *cess, cept,* and *clus.* The suffixes *-ion* and *-ive* are usually added to the variant forms *cess, cept,* and *clus.* For each word listed below, write related words ending in *-ion* and *-ive.* Use a dictionary if necessary.

|  | Related nouns ending in *-ion* | Related adjectives ending in *-ive* |
|---|---|---|
| 1. recede | _____ | _____ |
| 2. succeed | _____ | _____ |
| 3. include | _____ | _____ |
| 4. exclude | _____ | _____ |
| 5. receive | _____ | _____ |
| 6. deceive | _____ | _____ |
| 7. conclude | _____ | _____ |
| 8. perceive | _____ | _____ |

**Part B.** Words with the roots *cide* and *cise* often have a related form ending in *-ion.* Write the *-ion* form of the words below. Remember to add, drop, or change letters if necessary.

1. decide _____     3. precise _____

2. concise _____     4. excise _____

# 4 Words in Context: A Strategy for Homophones

The words *precede* and *proceed* sound almost alike, but they have different meanings. Two other pairs, *access* and *excess* and *accept* and *except* also sound alike but have different meanings.

**Part A.** Write a definition for each of these words. Use a dictionary if necessary.

access _____

excess _____

precede _____

proceed _____

accept _____

except _____

**Part B.** Fill in the blanks in the following sentences with one of the words below the blank. The word must make sense in the sentence.

1. I ironed all the clothes _____ Willie's.
   accept/except

2. He had been on a long trip the _____ year.
   preceding/proceeding

3. Was the winner there to _____ her award?
   accept/except

4. The _____ road leading to the ball field is full of ruts.
   access/excess

5. Do you remember who _____ you on the list?
   preceded/proceeded

6. I can eat anything _____ nuts and dairy products.
   accept/except

7. Darlene _____ to give directions to the stranger.
   preceded/proceeded

8. Delia cut off the _____ material before she hemmed the curtains.
   access/excess

## 5 The Roots *ceed* and *ceive*

The roots *ceed* and *ceive* present special spelling problems. *Ceed* sounds like *cede*. *Ceive* is hard to spell because *ei* is an unusual vowel pattern in English.

Sometimes, the easiest way to remember a spelling is to memorize it. There are only seven common words that contain the roots *ceed* or *ceive,* so you should try to memorize them. The seven words are all in Exercise 1.

The three words that have the root *ceed*:

_____     _____     _____

The four words that have the root *ceive*:

_____     _____     _____     _____

## 6 Challenge Word Building

On a separate piece of paper, combine the morphemes below to build at least 20 words. Use as few or as many morphemes as you need for each word. Use a dictionary if you are unsure of a word.

| Prefixes | | Roots | | Suffixes | |
|---|---|---|---|---|---|
| con- | in- | ceive/cept | cise | -ion | -ly |
| ex- | pre- | clude/clus | cess | -ive | |

## 7 Word Pyramid

Use the letters found in *cise* to complete the words below. Each word contains the letters *c, i, s,* and *e* at least once in any order. All of the words are used in this book.

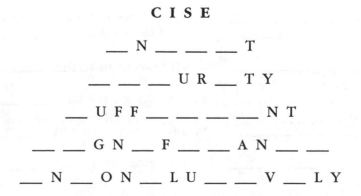

C I S E

__ N __ __ __ T

__ __ __ U R __ T Y

__ U F F __ __ __ __ N T

__ __ G N __ F __ __ A N __ __

__ N __ O N __ L U __ __ V __ L Y

# Lesson 30    Roots

*cur, dict, duce,* **and** *fer*

## 1 Recognizing Roots

In each group of words below, underline the roots listed on the left.

*cur*      *run*

current      cursive      recurring

curriculum      excursion      occurrence

*dict*      *say, speak*

dictate      verdict      addictive

dictionary      predictable      contradictory

*duce, duct*      *lead*

produce      introduce      reduce

product      introduction      conductor

*fer*      *carry, bring*

offer      different      referral

transfer      preferred      conference

## 2 Word Building

Join the morphemes that follow to build whole words. Write the words on the lines provided. Remember to drop the silent *e* if necessary.

1. con + cur _____

2. in + duce _____

3. e + duc + ate _____

4. in + fer + ence _____

5. vin + dict + ive _____

6. de + duct + ible _____

7. re + duct + ion _____

8. dif + fer + ent + ial _____

9. pro + duct + ive + ity _____

10. un + pre + dict + able _____

# 3 Reviewing Doubling Pattern 2

If a word has more than one syllable, look at the last one. If the last syllable has one vowel, ends in one consonant, and is accented, double the final consonant before adding a suffix that begins with a vowel.

**Part A.** When Doubling Pattern 2 is used with words that contain the root *fer,* it is more difficult to decide if the *r* should be doubled. That is because the accent sometimes shifts to a different syllable when a suffix is added.

Mark the accented syllable in the following words with an accent mark ( ´ ). Pronounce each word first. Then answer the questions that follow.

    con fer          con fer ral        con fer ence

1. In which two words is the second syllable accented? _____

2. In which word does the accent shift when the suffix is added? _____

3. In which word is the *r* doubled when the suffix is added? _____

4. In which word is the *r* not doubled when the suffix is added? _____

Fill in the blanks in this pattern.

**Pattern:** When a suffix is added to a word with the root *fer,* the *r* is doubled if the accent

stays on the _____ syllable. The *r* is not doubled if the accent shifts to the

_____ syllable.

**Part B.** Add the suffixes to the words below. Remember to pronounce the word with the suffix added to determine if the accent shifts. Use a dictionary if necessary.

1. occur + ing _____

2. refer + ence _____

3. prefer + ing _____

4. prefer + able _____

5. prefer + ence _____

6. refer + al _____

7. offer + ed _____

8. recur + ent _____

9. infer + ence _____

10. transfer + ing _____

## 4 The Suffixes *-ence* and *-ent*

Words with the roots *cur* and *fer* often have related words ending in *-ence* and *-ent*. Add *-ence* and *-ent* to the words below as indicated by the blanks. Write the new words on the lines provided. Remember to double the final *r* if necessary.

|  | -ence | -ent |
|---|---|---|
| 1. confer | _____ | |
| 2. prefer | _____ | |
| 3. differ | _____ | _____ |
| 4. refer | _____ | _____ |
| 5. recur | _____ | _____ |
| 6. concur | _____ | _____ |

Use two of the new words in original sentences.

_____

_____

## 5 Variant Forms

Words with the root *duce* often have related forms with the root *duct*. Remember that learning to recognize variant forms of roots can help you to develop spelling strategies. Beside each word below, write two related words that have the root *duct*. Use a dictionary if necessary.

**Related *duct* words**

| 1. induce | _____ | _____ |
|---|---|---|
| 2. produce | _____ | _____ |
| 3. introduce | _____ | _____ |
| 4. reproduce | _____ | _____ |

## 6 Adding Roots to Make Complete Words

Write one of the following roots in each blank below to make a whole word. The word must make sense in the phrase or sentence. Remember to drop the silent *e* if necessary. Then write the whole word on the right.

| cur | dict | duce/duct | fer |
|-----|------|-----------|-----|

**Whole words**

1. a foreign _____rency _____

2. an e_____ational program _____

3. There is a big dif_____ence. _____

4. the intro_____ion to the book _____

5. a monthly payroll de_____ion _____

6. They in_____red large expenses. _____

7. under the juris_____ion of the city _____

8. He was penalized for miscon_____. _____

## 7 Creating Words in Sentences

Combine the morphemes under each blank to create words that make sense in the following sentences. Remember to add or drop letters if necessary.

1. A _____ is a useful _____ book.
              ary  ion  dict                ence  re  fer

2. The police _____ who _____ the child.
              duce  de  ed             ab  ed  duct

3. The company will _____ _____ next year.
              duce  re             duct  ion  pro

4. The announcer _____ to the _____ weather.
              fer  ed  re            dict  un  able  pre

5. He likes to _____ his father just to be _____.
              dict  contra            dif  ent  fer

# Lesson 31 — Roots

### gress, ject, lect, mit, and mote

## 1 Recognizing Roots

In each group of words below, underline the roots listed on the left.

*gress*          *go, step*

| | | |
|---|---|---|
| progress | regressive | digression |
| congress | aggressive | transgression |

*ject*          *throw*

| | | |
|---|---|---|
| eject | dejected | objection |
| project | rejection | conjecture |

*lect*          *gather; choose;*          *read*

| | | |
|---|---|---|
| collect | election | lectern |
| recollection | selected | lecturer |

*mit, miss*          *send; let go*

| | | |
|---|---|---|
| admit | emit | permit |
| admission | transmission | permissive |

*mote*          *move*

| | | |
|---|---|---|
| motion | remote | promotion |
| unemotional | locomotive | automotive |

## 2 Word Building

Join the morphemes that follow to build whole words. Write the words on the lines provided. Remember to add or drop letters if necessary.

1. neg + lect _____     3. pro + gress + ive _____

2. ag + gress + ion _____     4. inter + mit + ent _____

5. sub + ject + ive _____

6. com + mit + ed _____

7. e + mote + ion _____

8. com + mote + ion _____

9. e + lect + or + ate _____

10. per + miss + ion _____

# 3 The Root *mit*

**Part A.** Verbs with the root *mit* often have related words with the root *miss*. The suffix *-ion* is usually added to the variant form *miss*. Beside each verb below, write the related noun ending in *-ion*.

1. admit _____

2. permit _____

3. submit _____

4. commit _____

5. omit _____

6. emit _____

7. remit _____

8. transmit _____

Use one pair of words in an original sentence.

_____

_____

**Part B.** The following words all end with the root *mit*, which has one vowel, one final consonant, and is accented. Combine the words and suffixes below and write the new words on the lines provided. Remember to double the final *t* if necessary.

1. permit + ed _____

2. submit + ing _____

3. admit + ance _____

4. submit + ed _____

5. commit + al _____

6. commit + ment _____

Now use two of the new words in original sentences.

_____

_____

## 4 Related Words

In each phrase or sentence below, underline the word ending in *-ion*. Then on the lines provided, write the verb ending in *gress, lect, ject,* or *mit* that is related to the word you underlined. The first one is done for you.

**Related verbs**

1. <u>transmission</u> fluid      transmit

2. presidential election      _____

3. What is your projection?      _____

4. The admission price is high.      _____

5. the progression from *A* to *Z*      _____

6. I have no objection to her visit.      _____

7. an interesting collection of tapes      _____

8. A small transgression will be forgiven.      _____

## 5 Changing Roots

Remove the root from each word below and replace it with one of the following roots. Write the new word on the line provided. Then use the word you have created in a phrase or sentence.

*gress*     *ject*     *lect*     *mit/miss*     *mote*

| | **New words** | **Phrases or sentences** |
|---|---|---|
| 1. pro*mote* | _____ | _____ |
| 2. re*gress*ion | _____ | _____ |
| 3. e*mot*ion | _____ | _____ |
| 4. sub*ject*ive | _____ | _____ |
| 5. *miss*ive | _____ | _____ |

# Lesson 32 — Roots

*form, pel, pend, plore,* and *pute*

## 1 Recognizing Roots

In each group of words below, underline the roots listed on the left.

*form*        *shape*

| | | |
|---|---|---|
| formal | conform | reform |
| uniform | transformer | information |

*pel, pulse*        *push, drive*

| | | |
|---|---|---|
| expel | repellent | impulse |
| compel | expulsion | propulsive |

*pend, pense*        *hang; weigh; pay*

| | | |
|---|---|---|
| suspense | dependent | indispensable |
| suspended | pendulum | compensation |

*plore*        *cry, wail*

| | | |
|---|---|---|
| implore | explore | imploring |
| deplore | unexplored | deplorable |

*pute*        *think, reckon; arrange*

| | | |
|---|---|---|
| dispute | imputed | deputy |
| computer | reputation | disreputable |

## 2 Word Building

Join the morphemes that follow to build whole words. Write the words on the lines provided. Remember to add, drop, or change letters if necessary.

1. pro + pel + er _____

2. ap + pend + ix _____

3. sus + pense + ion _____

4. per + form + ance _____

5. dis + re + pute _____    8. com + pulse + ive _____

6. com + pel + ing _____    9. ex + plore + ation _____

7. ex + pense + ive _____    10. ex + pend + it + ure _____

## 3 Variant Forms

Words with the root *pel* often have related words with the root *pulse*. Words with the root *pend* often have related words with the root *pense*. Beside each word below, write two words that have the variant form as a root. Remember that the variant form of the root is often used when *-ion* is added to a word. Use a dictionary if necessary.

1. repel         _____    _____

2. impel         _____    _____

3. expend        _____    _____

4. compel        _____    _____

5. suspend       _____    _____

## 4 Adding Roots to Make Complete Words

Write one of the following roots in each blank below to make a whole word. The word must make sense in the sentence. Then write the whole word on the right.

*form*     *pel/pulse*     *pend/pense*     *plore*     *pute*

**Whole words**

1. What a re_____ive smell!            _____

2. in a de_____able situation          _____

3. His victory was undis_____ed.       _____

4. a balloon sus_____ed in midair      _____

5. She gave a brilliant per_____ance.  _____

6. Insect re_____lent keeps bugs away. _____

## 5 Creating and Using Words

From each root listed below, create two words by adding prefixes or suffixes or both. Then use each word you form in a phrase or short sentence.

|  | Words | Phrases or sentences |
|---|---|---|
| 1. pend | _____ | _____ |
|  | _____ | _____ |
| 2. plore | _____ | _____ |
|  | _____ | _____ |
| 3. pel | _____ | _____ |
|  | _____ | _____ |
| 4. form | _____ | _____ |
|  | _____ | _____ |

## 6 Jumbled Morphemes

Combine the morphemes in each group below to create four different words. Use as few or as many morphemes as you need for each word. Remember to drop the silent *e* if necessary. Write the words on the lines provided.

1. de   in   pend   ly   ent   ence

_____          _____

_____          _____

2. dis   ed   pute   in   pense   able

_____          _____

_____          _____

3. re   able   pute   form   ation

_____          _____

_____          _____

# Lesson 33 — Roots

## 1 Recognizing Roots

In each group of words below, underline the roots listed on the left.

| reg, rect | *guide, rule* | | |
|---|---|---|---|
| | regular | regimen | irregular | incorrect |
| | regulate | deregulation | direction | correction |

| rupt | *break* | | |
|---|---|---|---|
| | rupture | disruptive | abruptly |
| | interrupt | corruption | eruption |

| scribe, script | *write* | | |
|---|---|---|---|
| | inscribe | subscribe | scripture |
| | describe | subscription | transcript |

| sist | *cause to stand, place; stop* | | |
|---|---|---|---|
| | persist | desist | consistent |
| | consistency | resistance | irresistible |

| spire | *breathe* | | |
|---|---|---|---|
| | inspire | transpire | spirit |
| | conspiracy | aspiration | respiration |

## 2 Word Building

Join the morphemes that follow to build whole words. Write the words on the lines provided. Remember to drop the silent *e* if necessary.

1. pre + scribe _____

2. bank + rupt _____

3. sub + sist + ence _____

4. non + de + script _____

5. reg + i + ment _____    8. inter + rupt + ion _____

6. in + sist + ent _____   9. mis + di + rect + ed _____

7. spire + ite + ual _____  10. in + de + scribe + able _____

## 3 Variant Forms

Words with the root *scribe* often have related words with the root *script*. Beside each word below, write two related words using the root *script*. Use a dictionary if necessary. Remember that the variant form of the root is often used when *-ion* is added to a word.

1. describe        _____    _____

2. prescribe       _____    _____

3. transcribe      _____    _____

## 4 Pattern Awareness

Most words with the root *sist* are followed by *-ent*, *-ence*, or *-ency*. Add the suffixes indicated at the top of each column below to the words on the left.

|            | -ent | -ence/-ency |
|------------|------|-------------|
| 1. insist  | _____ | _____ |
| 2. exist   | _____ | _____ |
| 3. persist | _____ | _____ |
| 4. consist | _____ | _____ |

There are two common exceptions to this pattern that you should memorize. *Assist* and *resist* are followed by *-ant* and *-ance*. Add *-ant* and *-ance* to the words below.

|            | -ant | -ance |
|------------|------|-------|
| 5. assist  | _____ | _____ |
| 6. resist  | _____ | _____ |

# 5 Adding Roots to Make Complete Words

Write one of the following roots in each blank below to make a whole word.
Remember to drop the silent *e* if necessary. Then use the word in a phrase or short
sentence.

*rect*     *rupt*     *scribe*     *sist*     *spire*

## Phrases or sentences

1. cor_____ed        _____

2. di_____ory        _____

3. tran_____or       _____

4. sub_____er        _____

5. con_____acy       _____

6. as_____ance       _____

7. indi_____ly       _____

8. unin_____ing      _____

# 6 Missing Links

Add a morpheme from this lesson that will link each pair below. The missing link will
form the end of the first word and the beginning of the second word. The number of
blanks indicates how many letters are in each missing link.

1. in   __ __ __ __   er

2. dis   __ __ __ __   ure

3. di   __ __ __ __   angle

4. cor   __ __ __ __   ified

5. con   __ __ __ __ __ __   ure

6. tran   __ __ __ __ __ __   writer

# Lesson  Roots

*sume, tract, turb,* **and** *vide*

## 1 Recognizing Roots

In each group of words below, underline the roots listed on the left.

*sume, sumpt*    *take; take up*

assume       presumably      consumer

resume       presumption     assumption

*tract*    *draw, pull*

tractor      subtract      attract

traction     contracted    distraction

*turb*    *confuse, agitate*

turbine      disturb      perturb

turbulent    disturbance   unperturbed

*vide, vise*    *see*

vision    video    revise    evidence

invisible   provide   television   provision

## 2 Word Building

Join the morphemes that follow to build whole words. Write the words on the lines provided. Remember to drop the silent *e* if necessary.

1. abs + tract _____
2. con + sume _____
3. turb + o + jet _____
4. sumpt + uous _____
5. ad + vise + ory _____
6. super + vise + or _____
7. un + at + tract + ive _____
8. un + dis + turb + ed _____
9. im + pro + vide + ent _____
10. sub + con + tract + or _____

## 3 Variant Forms

For each verb below, write a related noun that ends in *-ion*. Remember that the variant form of the root is often used before *-ion* is added to a word.

1. resume _____    5. revise _____

2. assume _____    6. provide _____

3. presume _____    7. televise _____

4. consume _____    8. supervise _____

## 4 Creating Words in Sentences

Combine the morphemes under each blank to create words that make sense in the following sentences. Remember to drop or change letters if necessary.

1. I don't have a recipe, so I'm _____.
<br> pro ing im vise

2. Read the description, then try to _____ the scene.
<br> ual vise ize

3. My son _____ a _____ amount of candy.
<br> s con sume      turb ing dis

4. It was _____ to have that tooth _____.
<br> vide pro ent      ed tract ex

5. If you're in the hospital, _____ are a good _____.
<br> it vise ors      ion tract dis

6. Let's _____ the _____ will be signed next week.
<br> sume as      con s tract

7. He was _____ by the _____ during the flight.
<br> per un ed turb      ence turb ul

8. It's a common _____ that everyone watches _____.
<br> ion as sumpt      vise tele ion

## 5 Looking at Meanings

Add one of the following roots to each partial word below. The word you create must fit the definition on the left. Use a dictionary if you are unsure of a word.

*sume*      *tract*      *turb*      *vise*

| Definitions | Partial words | Words with roots added |
|---|---|---|
| 1. to interrupt or bother | dis | _____ |
| 2. to give counsel | ad | _____ |
| 3. someone who comes to see you | itor | _____ |
| 4. to take up again | re | _____ |
| 5. to draw towards someone | at | _____ |

## 6 Changing Roots

Remove the root from each of the words below and replace it with one of the following roots. Then use the word you have created in a phrase or sentence.

*sume/sumpt*      *tract*      *turb*      *vide/vise*

| | New words | Phrases or sentences |
|---|---|---|
| 1. pre*fer* | _____ | _____ |
| 2. ex*pend* | _____ | _____ |
| 3. re*spire* | _____ | _____ |
| 4. dis*pose* | _____ | _____ |
| 5. pro*gress* | _____ | _____ |
| 6. de*mote* | _____ | _____ |
| 7. con*fus*ion | _____ | _____ |
| 8. sub*miss*ion | _____ | _____ |

## Roots Presented in This Unit

| | | | |
|---|---|---|---|
| cede | dict | mote | scribe |
| ceed | duce | pel | script |
| ceive | duct | pend | sist |
| cept | fer | pense | spire |
| cess | form | plore | sume |
| cide | gress | pulse | sumpt |
| cise | ject | pute | tract |
| clude | lect | rect | turb |
| clus | miss | reg | vide |
| cur | mit | rupt | vise |

## 1 Variant Forms

Some roots have variant forms. Knowing the variant form can help you to spell related words. In each of the following sentences, a verb form is italicized. Complete the sentence by writing the noun form of the same root in the blank provided. The first one is done for you.

1. You *deceived* me, and I dislike any form of __deception__.

2. If you *subscribe* to that new magazine, why not cancel your other _____ ?

3. I won't *permit* you to watch that movie even if your friends have _____.

4. If you *introduce* the speaker, I'll take care of the other _____.

5. Bread, eggs, and milk were *provided,* but we had to buy the other _____.

6. A bridge that's *suspended* over water or a gorge is a _____ bridge.

7. She *succeeded* in winning the tournament, so we celebrated her _____.

8. The driver *concluded* that he had room, but his _____ proved wrong.

## 2 Doubling Pattern 2

**Part A.** Underline the following roots in the phrases and sentences below. Notice whether the final consonant is doubled.

|  |  |  |  |
|---|---|---|---|
| *cur* | *fer* | *mit* | *pel* |

1. insect repellent
2. No admittance!
3. a useful reference
4. They're very different.
5. She's currently unemployed.
6. It started occurring yesterday.

7. a large remittance
8. a recurrent nightmare
9. a sincere commitment
10. I think blue is preferable.
11. That is a new radio transmitter.
12. She referred me to a new doctor.

**Part B.** Now fill in the blanks in the pattern below.

In words of more than one syllable, double the final consonant before adding a suffix that

begins with a vowel if the last syllable has _____ vowel, ends in one

_____, and is _____.

## 3 Adding Roots and Suffixes

**Part A.** Add *-ion* to the roots below. Write the new words on the lines provided. Remember to drop the silent *e* or use the variant form of the root if necessary.

1. regress _____
2. except _____
3. precise _____
4. process _____
5. reject _____
6. suspend _____

7. resume _____
8. correct _____
9. inscribe _____
10. aggress _____
11. retract _____
12. remit _____

**Part B.** Add the roots *ceed* or *ceive* to the following prefixes. Write the whole words on the lines provided.

1. pro _____     5. per _____

2. ex _____      6. con _____

3. suc _____     7. de _____

4. re _____

Remember that these are the only *ceed* and *ceive* words, so memorizing the spellings is the best strategy.

## 4 Practicing a Pattern: /ənt/, /əns/, and /ənsē/

Several roots in this unit can have the suffixes *-ant/-ance/-ancy* or *-ent/-ence/-ency* added to them. For each root on the left, check the correct column to show which suffixes can be added. Then write an example of the root with one of the suffixes added. Use a dictionary and remember to add, drop, or change letters if necessary.

| | -ant/-ance/-ancy | -ent/-ence/-ency | Example words |
|---|---|---|---|
| 1. differ | _____ | _____ | _____ |
| 2. repel | _____ | _____ | _____ |
| 3. recur | _____ | _____ | _____ |
| 4. insist | _____ | _____ | _____ |
| 5. incess | _____ | _____ | _____ |
| 6. inform | _____ | _____ | _____ |
| 7. accept | _____ | _____ | _____ |
| 8. disturb | _____ | _____ | _____ |
| 9. intermit | _____ | _____ | _____ |
| 10. depend | _____ | _____ | _____ |
| 11. precede | _____ | _____ | _____ |

## 5 Challenge Word Building

On a separate piece of paper, combine the morphemes below to build at least 20 words. Use as few or as many morphemes as you need for each word. Use a dictionary if you are unsure of a word.

| Prefixes | | Roots | Suffixes | |
|---|---|---|---|---|
| con- | re- | ceive/cept | -able | -ion |
| de- | sub- | mit/miss | -ible | -ive |
| per- | | scribe/script | -er | |

## 6 Missing Letters

A pair of letters has been omitted twice from each word below. The second time the letters are used they are reversed. Fill in the missing letters to make whole words. Each of the answers has a root from Unit 8. Study the example before you begin.

Example: <u>d</u> <u>e</u> ject <u>e</u> <u>d</u>

1. p ___ ___ f ___ ___

2. ___ ___ ndict ___ ___ e

3. un ___ ___ v ___ ___ ed

4. transm ___ ___ ___ ___ on

5. rep ___ ___ ___ ___ nt

6. ___ ___ plor ___ ___

7. subm ___ ___ ___ ___ ve

8. prop ___ ___ ___ ___ r

9. ___ ___ c ___ ___ sion

10. ___ ___ pt ___ ___ e

11. p ___ ___ spi ___ ___

12. in ___ ___ v ___ ___ ual

# 1 Patterns for Adding Suffixes

**Part A.** Fill in the blanks to complete the following sentences.

1. The silent *e* at the end of a root is dropped when a suffix that starts with a _____ is added.

2. If a word has one syllable, one vowel, and ends in one consonant, _____ the final consonant before adding an ending that begins with a vowel.

3. If the last syllable of a word has one vowel, ends in one consonant, and is _____, double the final consonant before adding an ending that begins with a vowel.

4. When adding a suffix to a word that ends in a consonant plus *y*, change the *y* to ____, unless the suffix begins with ____.

**Part B.** Join the morphemes that follow to build whole words. Remember to follow the patterns above.

1. ply + able _____
2. slip + ery _____
3. happy + ly _____
4. in + vent + or _____
5. pre + fer + ed _____
6. re + cur + ing _____
7. ad + mit + ance _____
8. as + sume + ing _____
9. com + pel + ing _____
10. con + fer + ence _____
11. im + prove + ment _____
12. ap + ply + cate + ion _____

# 2 Greek Morphemes

**Part A.** Fill in the blanks to complete the following sentences.

1. In words from Greek, /f/ is usually spelled _____.

2. In words from Greek, /k/ is usually spelled _____.

3. Greek words sometimes begin with a silent _____.

**Part B.** Many Greek morphemes function as combining forms. Combine the following morphemes to make 12 different words, and write them on the lines provided.

| | | | | |
|---|---|---|---|---|
| astro | geo | logy | photo | tele |
| bio | gram | meter | psycho | thermo |
| chrono | graph | phono/phone | techno | |

_____  _____  _____

_____  _____  _____

_____  _____  _____

_____  _____  _____

# 3 Adding Prefixes, Roots, or Suffixes to Make Complete Words

**Part A.** Add a root to each prefix or suffix below to create a word. Write the whole word on the right.

1. de _____
2. ex _____
3. re _____
4. in _____
5. im _____

6. di _____
7. ial _____
8. ious _____
9. ance _____
10. ion _____

**Part B.** Add at least one prefix and one suffix to each root below to create a word. Remember to add, change, or drop letters if necessary.

1. gress _____
2. pense _____
3. quest _____
4. plete _____
5. spire _____

6. sign _____
7. ject _____
8. mit _____
9. quire _____
10. pel _____

## 4 Spelling the Schwa Sound

Add one of the following suffixes to each word below. Write the new words on the lines provided. Remember to add, drop, or change letters and use a dictionary if necessary.

| *-ant* | *-ent* | *-able* | *-ate* | *-ery/-ary/-ory/-ry* |
|--------|--------|---------|--------|----------------------|
| *-ance/-ancy* | *-ence/-ency* | *-ible* | *-ite* | |

1. refer _____

2. assist _____

3. brave _____

4. insist _____

5. apply _____

6. digest _____

7. ignore _____

8. reduce _____

9. appear _____

10. expect _____

11. passion _____

12. defend _____

13. oppose _____

14. emerge _____

15. indulge _____

16. consider _____

17. moment _____

18. describe _____

## 5 Spelling /shən/, /shəl/, and /shəs/

Add one of the following suffixes to each root below and write the new words on the lines provided. Remember to add, drop, or change letters if necessary.

| *-ion* | *-ial* | *-ious* |
|--------|--------|---------|

1. race _____

2. caut _____

3. relax _____

4. infect _____

5. office _____

6. revise _____

7. benefit _____

8. essence _____

9. finance _____

10. convert _____

11. educate _____

12. persuade _____

## 6 Writing Sentences

Use three words from Exercise 4 and three words from Exercise 5 in original sentences.

_____

_____

_____

_____

_____

_____

## 7 Word Building

For each root on the left, build four words using any of the prefixes and suffixes given.

1. pose             -able   -al   de-   dis-   -ion   -ite   pro-   re-   sup-

_____     _____     _____     _____

2. cede/ceed       -ent   pre-   pro-   re-   sub-/suc-   -ure

_____     _____     _____     _____

3. verse            ad-   al-   con-   -ible   -ion   -ly   re-   trans-

_____     _____     _____     _____

4. scribe/script      con-   de-   -ion   pre-   pro-   sub-

_____     _____     _____     _____

# Glossary of Morphemes

## Prefixes

**a-**
without; on, in; in a state of

**ad-, ac-, af-, al-, ap-, as-, at-**
toward, to, near, or in

**anti-**
against, opposing

**auto-, aut-**
self

**bi-**
two

**con-, col-, com-, cor-**
with, together

**contra-**
against

**de-**
reverse, remove, reduce

**di-**
separation, twoness

**dis-, dif-**
absence; opposite;
reverse, remove

**ex-, ef-, e-**
out of, from

**in-, im-**
in

**in-, im-, il-, ir-**
not

**inter-**
between, among

**intra-**
inside, within

**intro-**
in, inward

**mis-**
wrongly, badly

**mono-, mon-**
one, alone

**multi-**
much, many

**ob-, oc-, of-, op-**
toward; against

**per-**
through; thoroughly

**poly-**
much, many

**post-**
after, later; behind

**pre-**
before

**pro-**
forth, forward

**re-**
back, again, anew

**sub-, sup-, suc-, suf-**
under; lesser

**super-, sur-**
superior, above; additional

**trans-**
across

**tri-**
three

**un-**
not, opposite of;
reverse an action

**uni-**
one

## Roots

**act**
do

**aero, aer**
air, of aircraft

**astro, ast**
star, constellation

**bio**
life

**ceed/cede, cess**
go

**ceive, cept**
take

**cent**
one hundred; center

**chrono, chron**
time

**cide, cise**
kill; cut

**clude, clus**
close, shut

**cord**
heart

**crat, cracy**
representative or
form of government, power

**cur**
run

**cure**
care

**cyclo, cycle**
circle, wheel

**dict**
say, speak

**duce, duct**
lead

**fact, fect, fit, fic(t)**
make, do

**fer**
carry, bring

**file**
line, thread; draw a line

**fine**
end

**form**
shape

**found, fund**
bottom; pour

**fuse**
pour; melt

**gen**
something produced; producer

**geo**
earth

**gram**
write, draw

**graph**
write, draw

**gress**
go, step

**ject**
throw

**lect**
gather; choose; read

**log(ue), logy**
word, speech; study of

**mand, mend**
entrust; order

**mechan**
machine

**merge, merse**
plunge, immerse, dip

**metro, metr, meter**
measure

**mit, miss**
send; let go

**mote**
move

**muse**
gaze, ponder; source of artistic inspiration

**pass, pat**
endure, suffer

**pel, pulse**
push, drive

**pend, pense**
hang; weigh; pay

**phono, phone, phon**
sound

**photo**
light

**plore**
cry, wail

**ply**
fold together; fill

**pone, pose, post, pound**
put, place

**port**
carry

**prove**
test

**psycho, psych**
mind, soul

**pute**
think, reckon; arrange

**quest, quer, quire**
seek, ask

**reg, rect**
guide, rule

**rupt**
break

**sane**
healthy

**scribe, script**
write

**sect**
cut

**serve**
keep, save; guard

**side**
sit, settle

**sign**
mark, sign

**sist**
cause to stand, place; stop

**sort**
chance, lot; go out

**spire**
breathe

**stance, stant**
stand

**sume, sumpt**
take; take up

**tail**
cut

**techno, techn**
art, skill, science

**tele**
distant

**ten, tain**
hold

**tend, tent, tense**
stretch

**test**
witness

**text**
weave, construct

**thermo, therm**
heat

**tour**
turn, around

**tract**
draw, pull

**turb**
confuse, agitate

**vent**
come, arrive

**verb**
word

**vert, verge, verse**
turn, bend, incline

**vide, vise**
see

## Suffixes

**-able**
able to, capable of, liable to

**-age**
action or result of an action;
collection; state

**-al**
relating to, characterized by

**-ance, -ancy**
state or quality of; action

**-ant**
inclined to; being in a
state of; someone who

**-ate**
cause, make; state, condition;
someone who

**-en**
made of; cause to be or have;
become

**-ence, -ency**
state or quality of; action

**-ent**
inclined to; being in a state of;
someone who

**-er**
more

**-er, -or**
someone who; something that

**-ery, -ary, -ory, -ry**
place where; collection,
condition, or practice of

**-est**
most

**-ful**
full of

**-hood**
state, quality, or condition of

**-ial**
relating to, characterized by

**-ian**
person who; of, relating to,
belonging to

**-ible**
able to, capable of, liable to

**-ic**
relating to, characterized by

**-ice**
state or quality of

**-ine**
of, pertaining to; chemical
substance

**-ion**
act, result, state of

**-ious**
full of, characterized by

**-ism**
act, condition, doctrine, or
practice of

**-ist**
someone who

**-ite**
quality of; follower or resident
of; mineral product

**-ive**
performing or tending toward
an action

**-ize**
cause to be or become

**-less**
without, lacking

**-ly**
in the manner of

**-ment**
state, act, or process of

**-ness**
state, quality, condition, or
degree of

**-ous**
full of, characterized by

**-ship**
state, quality, or
condition of; skill

**-ty, -ity**
state or quality of

**-ure**
act, process; function or body
performing a function

**-ward**
direction

**-y**
characterized by